WALLACE AND GROMIT'S
WORLD
OF
INVENTION

HarperCollins *Children's Books*

Based on the TV series commissioned by the BBC and created by Aardman Animations .

Executive Producers for Aardman:
Miles Bullough, Nick Park, David Sproxton, Peter Lord.

Executive Producers for BBC:
Alison Kirkham, Jacqueline Hewer.

Producers, Directors and Production Team:
Rob Baker, Merlin Crossingham
Roger Power, Ed Davies
John Woolley, Sybilla Wilson, David Ross.

Contributors:
Jem Stansfield, Kate Edwards, Dick Hansom, Neil Dunnicliffe, Ygraine Cadlock.

Very special thanks to:
Helen Neno, Tresta Baber.

Picture credits:

front cover, pp12-20, pp24-26, pp30-33, p42, p45, pp48-53, pp55-67, pp70-71, pp73-83, pp88-92, pp94-99, p106, pp108-111, pp114-121, p123, pp138-139, pp142-149, pp156-161, p166, pp170-175, pp178-181, pp186-189 © Getty Images
p14 © University of California Berkeley, Dept of Electrical Engineering & Computer Sciences
p14 © Fraunhofer IPA
p16 © IRobot
p21 © Leatherhead & District Local History Society
pp34-35 © Emily Cummins
p44, pp46-47, back cover © Cedric Lynch/Agni Motors
p66, pp162-167 © UK Intellectual Property Office
pp68 © Lightcraft Technologies Inc
front cover, p76 © Festo
p77, back cover © Professor Huosheng Hu, University of Essex, UK

p83, back cover © Daimler AG
pp102-103, pp107-108, pp112-113, p117, pp150-155, back cover © NASA
p122, pp124-126 © MAGENN Power Inc
pp138-143 © Stefan Hartmaier
p136, pp139-141 Martin-Baker Aircraft
p137 © Craig Penrice
pp178-179 Brainport Technologies, Wicab Inc
pp13 top right, 22, 23, 79, 109 insert Nova, pp110 insert left, 111 insert James Fischer for Aardman
pp26, 28 bottom right, 29 bottom right Alex Ntoya for Aardman
pp34 Helen Turton for Aardman
pp38-43 Timur Turgunov for Aardman
pp44 insert bottom left, 57, 159 bottom right, 163, 165-166, 175 inserts on R x 3, 190-191 main pic Luke Smith for Aardman

pp50 inset, 56 bottom right, 146-147 inset L, main picture back, inserts top and bottom on 147 Ash Mills for Aardman
p54 left inset Robert Morgan for Aardman
pp56 inset, 60 inset bottom left Kate Edwards for Aardman
pp72, 73 74, 78, 129 middle 2 images Sabine Hackenberg for Aardman
pp103 bottom right, 104-105 Rick Friedman for Aardman
p127 David Wright for Aardman
p171 Helene Ganichaud for Aardman
p173 bottom right Dave Alex Riddett for Aardman
p177 Trevor Owens for Aardman
pp182-183 Loïc de Guilly for Aardman

First published in the UK by HarperCollins Children's Books in 2010
1 3 5 7 9 10 8 6 4 2
ISBN 978-0-00-738218-7

Printed and bound in Italy
Colour reproduction by Dot Gradations Ltd, UK

WALLACE AND GROMIT'S
WORLD
OF
INVENTION

Written by Penny Worms

CONTENTS

FOREWORD

I can't tell you how delighted Wallace was when, after the many adventures they've had together, he and Gromit were finally asked to present their very own TV show – particularly when he found out it was going to be all about invention. "This is going to be the show that turns the cogs of cognition and squeezes the sauce into resourcefulness," he told me. Wallace has, of course, made quite a reputation for himself over the years for his cracking contraptions, and he was deeply honoured to get the opportunity to meet so many other famous inventors as he researched the programme.

It also inspired him to come up with a few new gadgets of his own, and gave him the chance to see how they measured up to the experts' – just as well Gromit was around to keep a wary eye on things when they looked as if they might go wrong. And they had a lot of fun trawling through the archives to discover some of the more ridiculous innovations from yesteryear.

But it's not just the famous inventors who made an impression on him – he soon discovered that boffins aren't just found in the laboratory. He came across many unsung geniuses who have used their imagination and creativity to come up with fantastic innovations to make life better for themselves and the people around them – from China, to Russia, to Africa. That's the thing about invention – it doesn't matter who you are, if you've got a great idea and a basic toolkit, you can turn it into a reality. And this book is full of amazing real-life inventors who did just that.

So really Wallace and Gromit's World of Invention isn't just about the discoveries you see on the show – it's about the spirit of Invention. And that's something we can all take into our everyday lives. If this book inspires just one person to come up with some ingenious new idea that can make the world a better place, then Wallace and Gromit will be happy to know their mission has been accomplished. (Especially if it's a new way to stop cheese going mouldy.)

Nick Park

WELCOME

"Hello readers, and welcome to our World of Invention. As you may know, I've made a bit of a name for myself as an inventor over the years, so you can imagine how chuffed Gromit and I were to be asked to present a TV show on that very topic. I've always believed in using technology to make life that little bit easier – my Techno-Trousers, the Knit-O-Matic and the dear old Robo-Chef are now the stuff of legend – so here was an opportunity to spread the word to the rest of the world. And now my dear friends at HarperCollins have had the brilliant idea of turning it all into a deluxe coffee table book. (I say, there's an idea Gromit – maybe if I screwed four legs onto it, we could use it as a coffee table too...!)

"So we've trawled through the archives to find some crazy contraptions which people thought would bring a bright new future, but which turned out to be a bit of a flash in the pan. And we've travelled to the far-flung corners of the world to meet some amazing inventors and their ingenious creations – from home-made helicopters to carnivorous clocks and even a robot penguin. (Better hope that Feathers McGraw doesn't see that one, eh lad?)

"But whether it's been a young lad in Africa making a windmill out of junk to bring electricity to his village or a British Rail boffin coming up with a design for a flying saucer, there's one thing that unites them all – the spirit of Invention. And that's something that you, dear reader, can share in too. We hope this book will inspire you to get your thinking cap on and start dreaming up ideas of your own. Take it from me, you don't have to be a genius to be an inventor!

"So sit back, put your feet up (but not on this rather lovely coffee table book, of course...) and prepare to be amazed as we explore the World of Invention..."

Chapter 01
HOME SWEET HOME

"Household chores, they never seem to end, do they readers? It is something that's taxed the brain of many an inventor over the years, myself included.

"So let me introduce you to the L.A.D. – my Labour Assisting Device – an automated dogsbody who's programmed to take care of every conceivable domestic duty. For instance, he can make a brew in half the time it takes Gromit – a significant improvement, wouldn't you say lad? You won't know what to do with yourself now that L.A.D.'s around!

"So in this chapter we're going to take a look at the little robotic helpers who make life around the home a piece of cake. At this rate, you'll soon be redundant, eh Gromit! Er, I say, what are you doing with that cup of tea, lad...?!?"

AMAZING HOUSEHOLD ROBOTS

We live in amazing times. Billion-dollar satellites cruise the skies above us and microscopic cameras reveal the deepest secrets of the human body. Every day, it seems as if science reaches new horizons. Which makes it all the more annoying that we still haven't figured out how to build a robot servant to do all our boring housework. Or have we?

Modern robots are a miracle of technology – capable of everything from playing the violin to carrying hospital patients from one bed to another.

Asimo

Asimo is the world's most advanced humanoid robot, built by car manufacturer Honda. Asimo is 130cm tall (the average height of a 9 or 10 year old child), and he can walk, run and climb up the stairs. He recognises faces and voices, and reacts to moving objects and human gestures. He runs on a rechargeable lithium battery and has a camera in his head.

This robot is very advanced and it has taken quite a while to reach this stage. The first domestic robots were a little less sophisticated – take George the Robot, for example.

> **Asimo stands for Advanced Step in Innovative Mobility.**

Tony Sale with George in 2010.

George the Robot

George was one of the first walking, talking robots made by 17-year-old inventor, Tony Sale. Tony built George in his bedroom in England in 1949 using Meccano, bits of an old radio and parts from a World War II crashed bomber. The following year, when Tony was in the Royal Air Force, he unveiled a shiny new George, built in 30 days and at a cost of £15. This new George was controlled by morse-code signals transmitted via radio waves. Tony would tap out code that made George turn his head, move his arms, and light up his eyes.

The invention was cutting-edge at the time and word spread quickly. Tony says, "I was a bit surprised by all the attention. George was just a little experiment really. He couldn't actually do any of the household chores – that was the media using a bit of artistic licence."

George's celebrity was short-lived, however. Soon newer, more sophisticated robots arrived, promising even greater labour-saving functions. George was consigned to history, and a quiet corner of Tony's garage. His retirement meant he never had to do a stitch of housework ever again. Lucky George!

While technology did improve over the next few years, progress was rather slower than anticipated.

George the Robot doing a spot of vacuuming in the 1950s.

MM7 (left) with his creator Claus Scholz.

Robot Robert

'Fire the maid!' was the Australian TV announcement when school teacher Bernard Smith unveiled Robert, his helpful household robot. Robert could do many chores – pour the tea, rock the baby, water the plants, vacuum the carpet, lift heavy objects – all without complaint.

Bernard built Robert using old aeroplane parts, metal shelving, lumps of wood, radio parts, two car batteries, 13 electric motors and 180 metres of wiring. His wheels came from Mustang fighter planes. All those people who saw Robert started to believe that robots could be the future. Any cynics were reminded that people laughed at the very first cars, and look what happened there!

MM7

Austrian Claus Scholz built the 'cybernetic Machine Selektor' MM7 as a remote-controlled 'servomechanical' robot – supposedly the answer to a housewife's dreams. MM stands for mechanical man. MM7 was rather scary looking and not something you would want standing around in your living room, but Scholz also suggested another purpose for his robot. He said that MM7 could handle firefighting and radioactive material just as easily as the vacuuming. For those activities, its looks were irrelevant! Claus Scholz had high ambitions for mechanical robots. He said, "What I eventually want to build is a machine that can virtually do any normal chore."

Left: A variety of household robots from around the world. 1. The Aero-Blue household robot from Japan. 2. A clothes-folding robot. 3. The Apri Attenda social partner robot that can distinguish voices and follow an individual around 4 A Motoman robot making pancakes. 5. A Care-O-bot, a mobile manipulation robot that can be used as a robotic butler!

Built for function

The early robots like George were inspirational and really caught the public's attention. But the obsession with making them humanoid was a bit of a red herring. The most practical designs bear no relation to the human form – they're built purely for function.

As science moved on, a new generation of robots emerged and instead of helping around the house they found other employment – working in our factories. Car plants are full of robots, lifting, assembling and painting our cars. In 1990, the idea of domestic robots was resurrected with the arrival of robot vacuum cleaners. They may not look much, but we finally had our first useful household robot.

Roomba

Roomba looks like a giant portable CD player, but it is actually a sensor-driven vacuum cleaner. You can set it off as you leave the house for the day, and come back to a dust-free floor. Roomba will figure out the size of a room and will readjust its cleaning pattern until it has covered the whole floor. It can slip under the sofa and into hard-to-reach places with ease. It is a robot without legs, arms or a head, but it is clever enough to clean your home, then switch itself off to recharge ready for tomorrow.

Nowadays, robots are everywhere, with 4 million of them tending lawns, cleaning homes and even cooking dinners. And according to most experts, the real robot revolution is only just beginning.

Colin Angle, a roboticist and the CEO of iRobot, the company that makes Roomba, says, "There have been a few false dawns, but I'm confident that the age of household robots really is finally upon us. Just think of all the automated gadgets we already have around the house – and that number is set to rocket over the coming decades."

Roomba.

Ri-Man

Ri-man is a Japanese robot built for use in hospitals to lift patients from their beds. As Japan's society ages and the nursing shortage gets worse, there will be a need for robots to help with heavy lifting. This test dummy is soft and gentle but very strong.

So while we wait for the day when every home has its own multi-purpose household robot, it's worth remembering that without pioneers like George's inventor, Tony Sale, the dream would still be a little more distant.

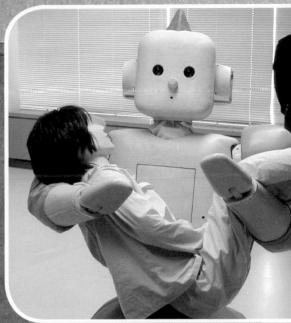

Ri-Man.

ROBOT FACTS

- The word "robot" came into use in 1923 from the English translation of a 1920 play by Karel Čapek. It is derived from the word robota, meaning "work" or "labour" in Czech and many Slavic languages.

- In 2003, it was estimated that there were 600,000 'household' robots in the world. These were mainly robot vacuum cleaners and lawn mowers. Today, it is claimed there are over four million.

- Japan is leading the way in robotics and 40% of robots are constructed in that country. However, the EU is not far behind.

- The EU currently spends about 50 million euros a year on research projects into robotics.

- As the market widens to include robots made for specialist and hazardous jobs as well as nanotechnology and artificial intelligence, it has been predicted that the sector will be worth more than US$66 billion by 2025.

THE WONDERFUL WORLD OF TEASMADES

A lovely hot cup of tea

Tea. It's what makes Britain great. And the Brits should know – drinking 166 million cups of it every day. It is the world's most popular drink, and now, alongside black tea, there is green tea, white tea, fruit tea, mint tea, caffeine-free tea . . . the list is endless. But black tea with milk and sugar is the drink that's been the most popular in Britain. So, it's not surprising that Britain's love of the cuppa has prompted some inventors to think up ways to make it automatically so they didn't even have to get out of bed!

The Gas-powered Automatic Tea Making Apparatus

Steam power was all the rage in the 19th century. Steam was powering factory machines, steam trains were puffing across the landscape, and the Stanley brothers were building their Stanley Steamer cars (cars that were powered by steam). So it's no surprise that the first teamaker was invented at this time, as a result of cutting-edge science. A man called Samuel Rowbottom from Derby applied for a patent for his 'Gas-powered Automatic Tea Making Apparatus' in 1891 – the first of its kind. It used a clockwork alarm clock, a gas ring and pilot light, and it worked by using steam from the boiling water to force the water out through a tube into a teapot.

A few years later another Englishman, Frank Clarke, bought a design from clockmaker Albert E Richardson and built a teamaker. His cleverly engineered model triggered a series of different movements – from striking a match to lifting a latch, which tipped up a kettle to pour in the water, hot and steaming, into a pot. When perfectly brewed, an alarm went off. Hey presto, a nice morning cuppa! Some say Frank Clarke should have won the Nobel Peace Prize – he was a gunmaker by trade but he encouraged people to stay in bed and make tea, not war. Noble ambitions indeed, but the invention didn't meet with widespread enthusiasm.

BRITAIN WAKES UP TO AUTOMATIC TEA

A story in pictures of a changing Britain. Already thousands of ordinary people enjoy this GOBLIN Service—soon it may become as normal a part of everyday life as a T.V. set or a washing machine.

The Marriotts used to have tea in bed *only* if Jack felt like going down to a cold kitchen to make it. Now they let Goblin Teasmade make the tea *whilst they sleep*, waking them on time when it's ready. Every morning they enjoy a fresh cup of tea in warmth and comfort.

Being an engine driver Jack Billing goes out and comes home at all hours of the day and night. "But," says Jack, "my Goblin Teasmade is always ready to supply a nice hot 'cuppa' just when I need it, getting up or coming home. That's service on the right lines for me!"

Mrs. Riley often missed the most exciting bit of the Television play whilst she was out in the kitchen making tea for the interval. But now, just a touch of the switch a few minutes beforehand, and tea is made automatically. It's equally helpful for bridge parties and social evenings.

For five years Mrs. Taylor has been a confirmed invalid. That meant waiting until her daughter came home before she had tea. Now Mary leaves Goblin Teasmade ready so that her mother has only to switch on and there's a fresh cup of tea to help pass the long afternoons.

THE MAGIC OF GOBLIN TEASMADE

Whilst you sleep it boils the water, makes the tea, lights the room and gently wakes you on time to freshly made tea. Wherever you are—whatever you do Goblin Teasmade will help by making tea or coffee automatically.

There are two models, Goblin Teasmade 'De Luxe' complete with teapot, electric kettle, electric clock and alarm, room lighting panels and tray; and 'Popular' a modified design using your own teapot.

Why not ask your Goblin dealer to show you

GOBLIN
Teasmade

'DE LUXE' MODEL £16.14.9 P.T. PAID
'POPULAR' MODEL £9.8.8 P.T. PAID
or on deferred terms

in the bedroom every night. By the time he's dressed (and collected his bag, there's a hot cup of tea (or coffee) waiting to send him off refreshed.

presents had been used the most, they would both say: "Our Goblin Teasmade!" For a young married couple out at work all day it's perfect. It's certainly an original gift, for weddings, Christmas or other occasions.

Or write to THE BRITISH VACUUM CLEANER & ENGINEERING CO. LTD. (DEPT. P.P.1), GOBLIN WORKS, LEATHERHEAD, SURREY
ALSO MAKERS OF GOBLIN VACUUM CLEANERS & WASHING MACHINES

17

Absolom's Teesmade

Then along came George Absolom. In 1932, he invented the Teesmade – the first electric tea maker – in his garden shed. His Teesmade used electricity to power the clock and heat the water. The steam inside the kettle forced the boiling water into the teapot. It was simple and safe.

However, even though Absolom's Teesmade came first, it was the Goblin Teasmade that really captured the imagination of the British public. By the 1970s, the teasmade was the most desirable domestic gadget around. It appeared at a time when most houses didn't have central heating, so it was a real luxury to have your morning cuppa in a nice warm bed – even if the machine did cost the equivalent of two weeks' wages!

1980s: the dream is over!

By the 1980s, however, the teasmade went out of fashion. Teasmades all over the country were consigned to the cupboard under the stairs, or dispatched to the Scouts' jumble sale, but some ended up, loved and cared for, in Sheridan Parsons' collection in Wootton Bassett, Wiltshire. She has 150 models that serve as a living timeline for the teasmade's 100 year history.

Sheridan says, "The thing is that devices like these not only show us how we look at science but also how we see our way of life – we don't even have five minutes for a cup of tea in the morning any more – it's all get up and go. I think it's a real shame."

Some of Sheridan Parsons' collection of teasmades.

We'll drink to that!

But maybe it's back again...

But teasmades haven't brewed their last cuppa. There has been a resurgence in demand, and electrical company Swan have recently brought out a new compact teasmade.

Sheridan says, "They were a symbol of everything that was good and right about Britain – and I'd love to see them return."

A modern teasmade.

23

WALLACE'S TOP 5 INVENTIONS FOR THE HOME

1. Now here's a handy item – the Portable Vacuum Cleaner, just the job for hoovering up litter from the gutter and getting into those tricky cracks in the pavement. Trouble is, there aren't many plug sockets on your average street corner...

I specialise in inventions to make everyday chores that little bit easier – from the Get-U-Up to my Jam-Ballista to the trusty Auto-Shopper. Needless to say, many others have followed my lead, and here are five of my favourite household gadgets which any inventor would be proud to have around the home.

2. And how about this inflatable apron? Those troublesome splashes and spills will just bounce off – and if your washing machine springs a leak, it doubles as a convenient buoyancy aid too!

3. Here's something for the all-round gardener - the Self-Guiding Lawnmower. The only thing is, you need an all-round garden too - as this contraption just keeps going round and round...

4. A bit short on that Get-Up-And-Go feeling first thing in the morning? Then what you need is this Automated Tea Spoon. One lump or two, it's bound to cause a stir!

5. It may look like this woman is taking a barrel for a walk, but in fact it's an early design for a washing machine. It looks like hard work to me!

FEATURED INVENTOR

Where are we? Oh yes, Malawi – we're off to Masitala Village, Wimbe, home to a young bright spark called William Kamkwamba, who's put the place into a bit of a spin with a revolutionary new idea to light up his community...

William Kamkwamba, AKA 'Windmill Boy'

We all tend to take our home comforts for granted. It's easy to forget how lucky we are to have simple things like lights at the flick of a switch, hot and cold water from a tap and heating when it's cold outside. If you've ever been without water or electricity for even a short time you know how inconvenient it is, so just imagine what you'd do if you had to create your own energy and water supplies from whatever bits and pieces you had to hand – odds and ends of wood, some scrap metal and a used drainpipe for instance. That was just the challenge facing 14-year-old Malawian William Kamkwamba back in 2001.

William lived in Masitala Village, Wimbe, a small farming village in Malawi. Only 2% of the nation had electricity and fresh water was in short supply. To make matters worse, in 2001 a severe drought hit the area, causing crop failure and terrible famine.

When the drought hit and William's family had no crops to sell, they couldn't afford to continue sending him to school. He kept himself busy by going to the library and reading books, particularly on science and engineering, to try to help himself, his family and his village. William sometimes found it hard to understand the English, but one day he happened upon a book that changed his life. It was called *Using Energy*, by Professor Mary D. Atwater, and it explained, in simple terms, how energy is all around us and just needs to be converted to another form before it is useful.

William had never even heard of a windmill, but reading the book he learned how windmills can harness energy from nature and was inspired to try to help his village with such an invention. He built a small model from bamboo, a plastic lid and parts of a flip-flop but the thing he really needed was a dynamo. William salvaged one from an old bicycle.

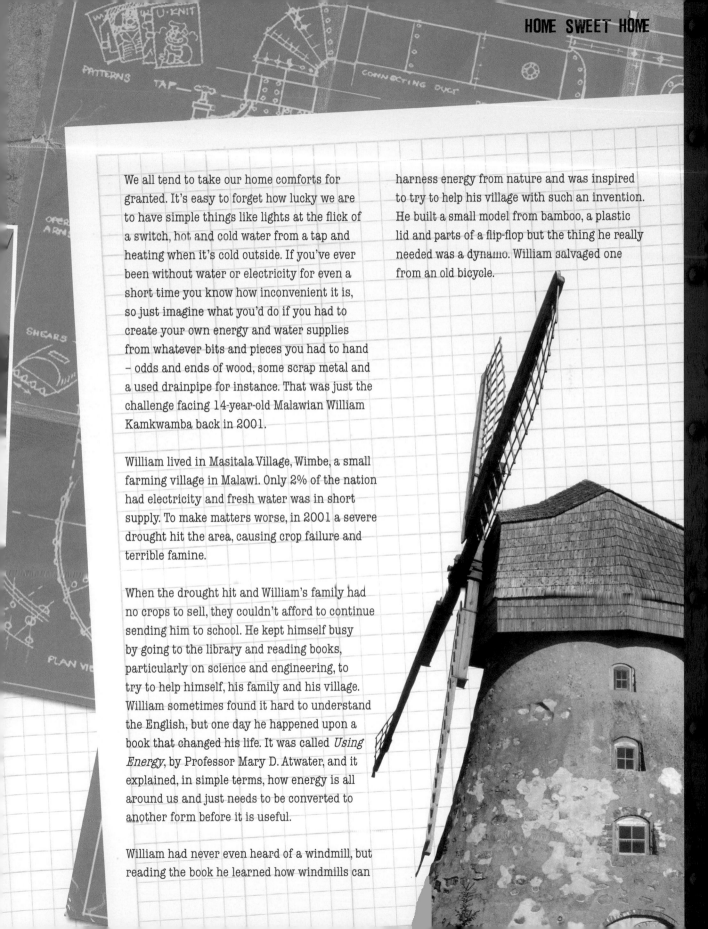

A dynamo converts mechanical energy (for example from a windmill or water turning a wheel) into an electrical current using a magnetic coil.

William was then ready to build the real thing. "I had a picture of it in my mind. All I needed was the parts. I used a broken bicycle frame for the shaft, beer bottle caps as washers, pieces of bamboo and PVC pipe for the blades." But the first time he tried the windmill and dynamo, the blades went round so fast that it blew up his radio! That was the first of many setbacks as William figured out the laws of electronics, mainly through trial and error with many experiments. Every problem taught William a new lesson. One thing he learned was how to lower the voltage of the current by sending the electricity through a long copper wire wrapped around a stick. This meant enough power was lost to play the radio without destroying it. At last his experiment was ready to put into operation for the whole village.

William says, "I remember the excitement of seeing the windmill for the first time. The whole village came to see. When it worked and the lightbulb came on, everybody cheered!"

An early dynamo.

William's windmill.

Electric wind

Because windmills were not widely known in Malawi, there wasn't even a word for it in the language. William called it a *magetsi a mphepo*, literally electric wind!

So, from a pile of old junk, a young boy brought power to his village for the first time, but this was just the start of his ambitions. As William's knowledge grew, so did the scale and ambition of his ideas. The windmill was extended to a height of 12 metres to catch the wind above the trees and later two more windmills were built. William also made a transformer and plug socket, along with a circuit-breaker to stop it from overheating. He also built an electric cooker – with a wire that heats up and boils water. And to get the water, he built a pump, which not only provides supplies for cooking but also helps to irrigate the ground so that crops can be grown more successfully.

World fame!

William's fame spread, not only in his village, but also across the world. In 2006 a reporter interviewed him and after that he was invited to conferences and other events and onto TV shows in America and other countries. Following this media interest William won a scholarship to the prestigious African Leadership Academy, which in turn led to a place at Dartmouth College in the US. In 2009, a book was published about William, *The Boy Who Harnessed the Wind*, which became a *New York Times* bestseller.

But, despite his worldwide fame, William's main focus is still on the community in which he was born. He explains, "My most recent projects have been solar panels for the local school, a deep water well and a solar-powered pump to provide clean water."

William's story is an inspiration for all budding inventors. He says, "In science we invent and create, we make new things that can benefit our situation," and if we can all invent something useful and put it to work, we can help to change the world.

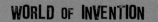

Would you believe it? Even the most famous inventors can sometimes come up with an idea that gets a cool reception...

Never Got off the Drawing Board...

EINSTEIN'S FRIDGE

If you were to ask yourself which modern household device has had the most impact on your life, you would probably say your mobile phone, your computer or perhaps your TV. The chances are that your list would be fairly long before you got to that white box in the kitchen that stops your milk from going off. But that box has meant you now live a healthier and longer life than your predecessors. That is not something you can say about your mobile phone!

It is a fact that 20th century refrigeration has changed the world. For the first time, people could safely store large amounts of fresh food, drink and even medicines, eliminating disease and hugely increasing the quality of our diet. Refrigeration technology is employed in practically every type of industry, including the oil industry and microchip technology.

In little over a century, human beings went from hauling blocks of ice from one place to another to prevent food from spoiling to being able to go skiing in midsummer. Snow-making machines work in the same way as a common fridge; both use a process called a vapour compression cycle. This is based on one of the principles of physics – when a liquid is rapidly vaporized (through compression or squeezing), it means that it turns into a rapidly expanding vapour, or gas, which draws in energy from the surrounding area. Fridges have an expansion device that evaporates coolant into a gas. Then it pumps the gas around a network of pipes and chambers. As the gas slowly turns back into liquid form, it absorbs energy in the form of heat, cooling the air inside. The process continues over and over again, keeping the contents of your fridge cold.

The absorption fridge

This basic technology has been the same for nearly a century, but in the early days, the liquid coolants used were often highly toxic. In the 1920s, a newspaper reported the death of a Berlin family who were asphyxiated while they slept because their refrigerator, full of methyl chloride, had sprung a leak. This news prompted one eminent physicist to turn his mind away from his theory of relativity to work on a new fridge design. That physicist was Albert Einstein.

Einstein worked with colleague Leó Szilárd to come up with a completely new fridge design with no working parts at all. It just needed a heat source. This meant there was no pump squeezing and squashing poisonous chemicals round some rickety and potentially leaky pipes.

Instead, Einstein's fridge used pressurised gases and a continual chemical process to keep things cold. The fridge had chambers containing butane, water and ammonia, which reacted together to create the same kind of cycle as a vapour compression fridge, drawing heat out of the cooling chamber.

Einstein and Szilárd called their invention an 'absorption fridge' and applied for a patent in 1930. What was so revolutionary was that the fridge needed no electricity – which was useful back then, when supply was unreliable and power cuts were common.

As successful and clever as the absorption fridge was, it turned out to be one of Einstein's rare failures. The manufacturers of compression fridges kept improving the technology so they became safer and cheaper. Instead of redesigning the fridge, they found better coolants, chlorofluorocarbons (CFCs).

Fridge manufacturers started using CFCs decades ago, but now they are having to look for alternatives. Studies have shown that they are very harmful to the environment, contributing to the greenhouse gases that scientists believe are causing global warming. That is why fridges are specially recycled, to prevent the release of those harmful gases into the air. So, after 80 years, people are looking at Einstein's idea for a fridge again.

A working model

Dr Malcolm MacCulloch and his team at Oxford University have actually built a version of Einstein's fridge. And if they can successfully get the design off the drawing board and into our kitchens, they will have helped to solve a pretty basic problem with conventional fridge design – their insatiable need for electrical power. It is estimated that fridges account for around 10% of the average household's electricity bill. What Dr MacCulloch's team hope is that they can quadruple the efficiency of the fridge and generate the heat they need from solar power. No electricity and no CFCs will mean a great deal to the environment, but for a quarter of the world's population who have no access to electricity, Einstein's fridge could be a lifesaver.

Dr MacCulloch says, "You can see the possible value of a device like this – where we can store fresh supplies and medicine in areas where they are needed the most."

Albert Einstein.

Emily Cummins prepares a prototype model of her fridge.

The scrap metal fridge

If the idea of Albert Einstein as an inventor of a fridge seems a little odd, then the next development in fridge design seems downright unbelievable. It takes us from Albert Einstein, Professor of Theoretical Physics in Germany, to Emily Cummins, 22-year-old British student. Emily has designed a fridge that is every bit as revolutionary as Einstein's. Like Einstein's design, Emily's fridge has no moving parts and can be used almost anywhere, but hers is even more simple than Einstein's. What's more, it can be built from scrap metal – anything from old oil cans to discarded car parts.

Easy to make

All you need are two metal cylinders – one inside the other. The larger outer cylinder should have holes to allow evaporation. The space between the two cylinders is then filled with soil or sand and soaked with water, which doesn't even need to be clean. As the fridge sits in a warm environment, the water evaporates away, sucking energy from its surroundings as it does so. This leaves the middle chamber nice and cold. To keep this fridge 'on', you refill the chamber with water every once in a while, just like watering a plant. It is simple, safe, easy to build and fantastically practical for use in hot countries, for storing things like medicine.

Emily says, "The basic idea is so simple. When you look at nature, it's how we cool things biologically – just like sweating."

When Emily travelled to Namibia on a gap year, she showed people her fridge design and watched as they built one for themselves from bits of scrap. Their resourcefulness amazed and impressed her. She soon became known as 'the fridge lady' by the locals, whilst back home she started to win awards. Turning the energy-hungry, polluting white boxes in our kitchens into completely green appliances is a tall order for any inventor. Hopefully, Malcolm and Emily will succeed in the challenge – for the sake of our environment and for those people in developing countries who want a better and healthier lifestyle.

Emily with a group of children in Namibia.

Chapter 02
GETTING FROM A TO B

"Next up, we're going to be looking at some rather unusual forms of transport – these days there are so many ways of getting from A to B that you hardly need to use your legs at all. We'll be finding out about electric motorbikes, a vacuum-powered railway and a top-secret UFO designed by British Rail, no less. So all aboard, as we set off on a transport of delight!"

THE AMAZING PEDAL-POWERED SUBMARINE

Here's a vehicle that not only goes from A to B, but takes you under the C as well. Under the C! See what I did there, readers?

During the highly oppressive Soviet rule of Leonid Brezhnev from 1964 to 1982 many Russian people turned to inventing to try to make their lives better. During Brezhnev's time in government, people's freedoms were very restricted and they needed permission to do just about everything. They had to work hard for the good of the country and there was little tolerance for individual creativity or original thought. It was also a time of extreme poverty for many Russians.

With no freedom and no money, inventors in Russia started to dream of a better life. Unable to accept their fates or the dreariness of the future ahead of them, they began to think of ways to escape – building home-made submarines, planes and even underground trains.

Pedal power

Mikhail Puchkov started to build a pedal-driven submarine in 1981. He worked in his attic, away from the prying eyes of neighbours whose gossip could have been his downfall. If the authorities, such as the police, found out what he was doing, they may have seized the parts he had struggled so hard to get. They might even have arrested him. Mikhail just worked quietly and secretly until he had built something he thought might work. When he tested it in 1984 in a nearby river, it sank like a stone. Undeterred, Mikhail continued to improve his submarine, testing it under the cover of night, until it was watertight.

Mikhail's first long-distance test at sea was a 30-kilometre round trip to a nearby island. He pedalled all the way.

He says, "I was covered in sweat, my muscles ached, and I was constantly afraid of springing a leak. The voyage took 18 hours in total. When I got back, I decided to get an engine."

Mikhail Puchkov peering out of his home-made submarine.

Can you imagine being submerged under the sea in a home-made submarine so small that you aren't able to stretch out, stand up or move around for 18 hours, relying on a thin air pipe breaking above the water to stop you from suffocating?

Can you imagine pedalling for hours to get to an island that is a military base – which means that you can't get out and look around, you just have to head straight back? For most of us, the idea seems like madness, but this was just the first of many voyages for Mikhail.

Captured

Unfortunately, during one such voyage, Mikhail's submarine got caught in a net. He was rescued, but the KGB seized his submarine and arrested him for spying. Somehow, Mikhail managed to make them believe his story and after two days they let him go. In fact, they even recommended him for a place at the St Petersburg Shipbuilding Institute so he could learn more.

With the skills he learned at the Institute, he continued to improve his submarine. It is much bigger and more comfortable now, with thicker glass so he can dive deeper and an electronic navigation system. It can now travel up to 160 kilometres a day and has a top speed of 6km/h. What's more, it is legal and licensed, making Mikhail the only owner of a private submarine in Russia.

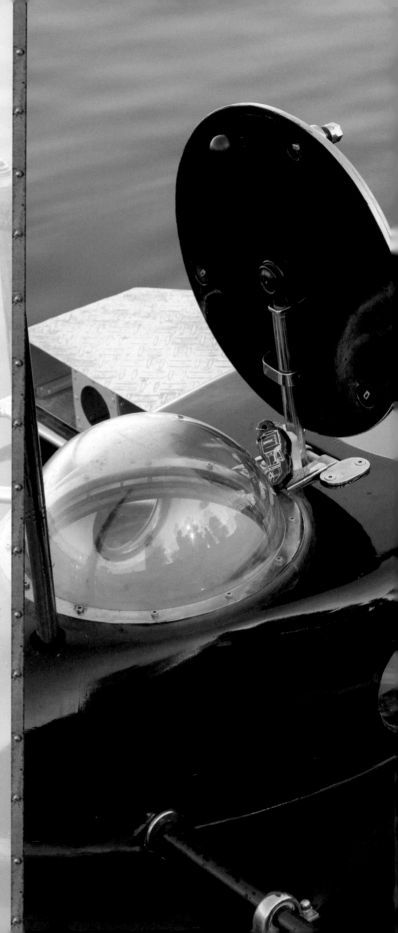

Main pic: Mikhail Puchkov's new and improved submarine in the water.
Above: The control panel of the sub.

Mikhail's submarine has been his life's work and passion, but he's not finished yet. He wants to make the outer surface thicker so it can submerge to greater depths, possibly even 30 metres. Now, Mikhail can go across the Gulf of Finland from St Petersburg to Helsinki in Finland and back again. He hopes one day to go even farther – perhaps around the world.

"I want to share my invention with everyone," he says. "Maybe I'll paint it yellow and come to Liverpool!"

THE PEDAL-POWERED SUBMARINE

- has taken 25 years to build
- has a maximum speed of 6km/h
- can reach a depth of 10 metres
- used to be pedal driven but now it has one electric engine and two petrol engines. Mikhail hopes to convert it to diesel in the future
- can carry one additional passenger
- is able to stay under water for two hours and can travel 12km in that time. It can do this three or four times on one charge.

Here's a man with a plan on the Isle of Man...

CEDRIC LYNCH AND HIS ELECTRIC MOTORBIKES

The TT Race on the Isle of Man is one of the biggest events in the motorsport calendar. It is a superbike Grand Prix, to which thousands of motorbike fans flood every year. Traditionally, they come to see the most skilful riders on the fastest road bikes in the world, but in recent years, a new event has been added to the TT race schedule – the TT Zero.

Even motorsport is thinking green, as this is a race for motorcycles which are powered without the use of carbon-based fuels and have zero toxic or noxious emissions. The race tends to be ridden on specially-engineered electric bikes. As the Earth's oil stocks dwindle, electric motors are being taken more seriously. International companies with multi-million pound budgets are investing in new technologies, all eager to discover something that might replace the petrol-driven combustion engine.

Standing on the grid at the TT Zero, next to some expensively engineered machines, are the more humble bikes from the team of Agni Motors. What this team lacks in investment it more than makes up for in passion and ingenuity, led by the talents of one Cedric Lynch.

Cedric says, "At the age of 5 my parents bought me a book that explained how a child could make an electric motor from various household items. I was hooked. I left school at 12 but carried on studying the subjects that interested me - mostly science."

Souper-charged

At the age of 24, Cedric entered a competition to design a vehicle that could travel the farthest on only two small car batteries. Cedric's vehicle was powered by a home-made motor, in part made out of flattened soup cans. It came second out of 50 competitors.

Cedric Lynch today on one of his electric motorbikes.

Above: Cedric racing in the early 1980s.
Opposite: A competitor in the TT Zero.

HONDA
VisitIsleofMan.com
103
102
105
104
50
Thompson Flooring

Spurred on by this success, Cedric entered more competitions for electric vehicles, teamed with rider, Arvind Rabadia. It was a partnership that was to last, not least because Arvind kept on winning! Arvind says, "I won 90% of the races because Cedric's motors were the best."

Arvind Rabadia on a converted Kinetic Blaze.

Lynch's motor was unique because of its engineering. An electric motor uses magnets and their attracting and repelling forces to create motion. Often magnets are fixed inside the casing of an electric motor and an electro-magnet coil called an armature is fitted onto the rotating spindle. When an electric current passes through the armature (often a coil of wire around a metal fitting), an electric field is generated which forces the armature to rotate. What is unique about Cedric's motor is that it has a disc armature not a coiled one, which means that it has magnets on both sides. This doubles the available flux density and shortens the magnetic path, meaning that it is more powerful for its size than any other motor engine technology.

Better, faster motors!

Cedric's talents were quickly becoming noticed. He entered into a business deal, but it didn't work out. It was a hard time for him, but his old friend, Arvind, came up with an idea. He suggested they go to India to set up a factory to make an even better version of his motor, and Agni Motors was born.

The motor designed by Cedric and Arvind is more powerful and more efficient than the previous model – about 92% of the battery power is converted into propulsion and only 8% into heat. Compare that with an approximate 30% efficiency of a petrol engine! They are now making 1,000 motors a year with a variety of uses – powering machines such as go-karts, mobility vehicles, pumps, cranes and boats.

With the business up and running, Cedric and Arvind decided to return to their first love – racing. When they heard about the TT Zero race in 2009, it was a challenge they couldn't refuse. Racing brought them together in the first place and so they decided to give it a go. They found experienced racer Robert Barber, who suggested they customise an existing motorcycle and he arranged for them to buy one without its petrol engine. Converting the bike into an electric racing machine was an easy process for the team and Rob Barber found the handling was not very different from his regular racing bike.

Agni Motors' electric racing motorcycle.

THE TT ZERO STATS

The course is almost 38 miles (61km) long on very hilly public roads in the Isle of Man.

Team Agni 2009
Time: 25m 53.5s
Fastest lap: 87.43mph
Top speed: 102mph
Winning margin: 3m 11s

Team Agni 2010
Time: 25m 21s
Fastest lap: 89.29mph
Top speed: 104.20mph

Team MotoCzysz 2010
Time: 23m 22.89s
Fastest lap: 96.82mph
Top speed: 135mph
Winning margin: 1m 59s

In 2010, Team MotoCzysz narrowly missed out on a £10,000 prize put up by the Isle of Man Government for the first team to record a 100mph lap.

The Agni team triumphed, crossing the line three minutes before the next competitor. They were the winners of the first ever zero carbon race.

In the 2010 race, the team smashed their time and top speed but were unfortunately beaten by American team, MotoCzysz. Nevertheless, this defeat shouldn't dampen the Agni spirit. With a team like theirs and Cedric's ingenuity, they'll no doubt be competing in the next TT race. So, don't forget to keep an eye out for them – they are sure to be out in front.

Looks like he's got the electric motor down to a TT, eh lad!

WALLACE'S TOP 5 METHODS OF UNRELIABLE TRANSPORT

1. This may look like an over-sized hamster wheel, but it is in fact the Dynosphere – and its inventor, Dr Purves, had plans to build one big enough to transport five people. Well, if you ask me, he must have been a few wheels short of a shopping trolley...

As anyone who's ever waited for the Number 39 bus can tell you, transport isn't always 100% reliable. So fasten your seatbelts as we take a look at some of the worst offenders.

2. Surf's up! Just goes to show that you don't have be a beach bum to enjoy a bit of surfing – a well-pressed suit is much smarter than those baggy shorts, don't you think?

3. Talk about mobile homes! Most people prefer to park their cars outside their houses, not underneath them...

4. Who needs a car when you can give three friends a lift on your bike? Very eco friendly, but you need a good sense of balance – and watch out for those low bridges!

5. Like the old song almost said, these boats were made for walking. A pair of canoe shoes – fancy that! Don't look very safe to me though...

49

FEATURED INVENTOR

Now we're going to give a high 5 to the man who brought us the C5. It's our featured inventor, Sir Clive Sinclair.

SIR CLIVE SINCLAIR

Sir Clive Sinclair is a pioneer inventor, trailblazer and electronics genius, who has experienced both the highs and lows of being an inventor. He was well-known and well-respected in the UK in the 1970s and 80s, but too few of us remember his illustrious inventing career. We just remember him as the inventor of his biggest flop – the C5.

Clive with his C5 electric vehicle.

Clive with his pocket television in 1981.

The C5 was an electric one-man vehicle that was so badly received by the press and the public that it became an object of ridicule. For Sir Clive, it was a disaster. He had sunk many millions into its development, a fortune he had built up from his other successful inventions – including miniature radios and televisions, the pocket calculator, digital watches and the first affordable home computer.

Sir Clive says that he was never in it for the money. He just wanted to invent things that he thought ought to exist; things that people didn't even know they needed. That was one of the reasons he became an inventor in the first place. When he was six years of age he saw a TV programme in which an inventor made paint that changed colour as he applied it. The idea made such an impression on the young Clive that he decided, then and there, that an inventor would be a very good thing to be.

The pocket calculator

Everyone now takes the pocket calculator for granted, but the invention of Sinclair's Executive Pocket Calculator in 1972 was way ahead of its time. The Executive was small, slimline and affordable. Previously, people used old-fashioned mathematical equipment such as slide rules, logarithm books and big calculating machines to do complicated sums. They had to rely on their brains to do the more simple stuff! The only calculators that existed were large desk-top versions for the office.

It's curious to think that one leading retailer actually told Sir Clive that people wouldn't want his invention. Luckily, the retailer Boots thought differently and as soon as they put it on sale, it was a huge success. Apart from its size and price, the other truly stand-out feature on the Executive was the groundbreaking LED (Light Emitting Diode) display. Sir Clive went on to launch further pocket calculators, including the Cambridge Memory Calculator. The LED display on his calculators was a first, and led Sir Clive to another of his inventions – the digital watch.

The Sinclair Cambridge Memory Calculator, launched in 1973.

The Sinclair ZX-80 home computer.

Home computing

The Sinclair ZX-80 home computer really established Sir Clive as the best of British Inventors. People could buy computers at the time, but they cost around £500, which is roughly equivalent to £1,500 nowadays. Sir Clive's vision was that computers should be available to all and he set out to design a cheaper version from scratch – bit by bit.

When he unveiled the ZX-80 in 1980, it cost under £100. The response was phenomenal, selling many thousands a month at its peak. This computer was state of the art at the time. You could just plug it into your TV set and a whole new world of computing and data storage was available to you. The ZX-80 made Sir Clive very famous and wealthy, but his other passion was about to cost him dearly.

The C5

It had always been Sir Clive's dream to make the perfect electric vehicle. Even though they are non-polluting, that wasn't what inspired him. It was the quiet simplicity and elegance of electric over petrol-driven or diesel-driven cars. Launched in 1985, and costing only £399, Sir Clive hoped the C5 would revolutionize personal transport in Britain. The revolution, however, stalled before it began, partly because the batteries struggled to last more than 10 miles. So, instead of millions of C5s gliding silently and elegantly around our streets, they ended up discounted, discarded and discontinued.

"It's all part of being an inventor," Sir Clive said. "You have to accept failure as you do success – even if the failures can prove to be more expensive."

The C5 has gained something of a cult following, as this collection at a rally in the UK shows.

Tesla Roadster - an electric sports car.

The electric revolution

Despite this set back, Sir Clive continued to chase his electric dreams, with inventions like the Zike, an electric bicycle, and the Zeta, a low-cost motor that could convert a normal bicycle to an electric one. Neither caught on, but 20 years later, most major car manufacturers are now chasing their own electric dreams. Electric vehicles have finally sparked the public imagination, and no one could be happier than Sir Clive.

"It seems that it's an idea whose time has finally come," said Sir Clive. "This is the decade for the electric vehicle."

And despite his previously bumpy ride, Sir Clive is back for another crack at the electric vehicle revolution. The X-1 is a new electrically-assisted recumbent bicycle that he hopes will make his dream a reality. Maybe, 25 years on from the C5, his time might have finally come.

Sir Clive's new electric vehicle, the X-1.

Did you know that in the age of the steam train, one of our greatest British inventors came up with an alternative way to make the railways run on time? Sadly, it never got off the drawing board...

Never Got off the Drawing Board...

BRUNEL'S ATMOSPHERIC RAILWAY

If you've ever made a long journey in Britain, the chances are you've been on, over or in something that was either built or inspired by Isambard Kingdom Brunel.

And this, the Clifton Suspension Bridge . . .

In just one city, he built this, the SS Great Britain . . .

And this, Bristol Temple Meads Station . . .

Brunel was born in 1806 and at a very early age he learnt the basic principles of engineering. He became an engineer and architect who in just 50 years transformed Britain. His bridges spanned impassable gorges, his ships conquered the seas and his railways brought cities closer together.

He was at the very heart of the great railway expansion of the 1800s and in 1833 was appointed chief engineer on the Great Western Railway, which linked London to South Wales and all the towns in between. His railway was a triumph, but not everything he touched turned into engineering gold.

When asked to build a new line in South Devon, Brunel came up against two problems – sharp turns and steep hills. Early locomotives had difficulties with both, so Brunel had to think of another way to pull passenger cars. But how could a train of passenger cars be propelled forward without an engine? Brunel decided the track itself could do the work, so he turned to a new technology and decided to build an 'atmospheric railway'. He visited one in operation in Dublin and managed to convince the South Devon Railway that it was the perfect system for them. It was a brave and risky decision, but people felt that if anyone could do it, Brunel could.

SO WHAT IS AN ATMOSPHERIC RAILWAY?

An atmospheric railway literally moves along on air. Train carriages are mounted on pistons housed inside a sealed pipe. A series of steam engines along the line removes some of the air from inside the pipe, creating a vacuum in the direction of travel. The difference in air pressure causes the train to be pushed forward by the stronger air pressure behind the piston. This is the principle behind atmospheric railways.

Jem Stansfield (right) and Brunel expert Robert Hulse at Didcot Railway Station admiring the last remaining section of Brunel's doomed atmospheric railway.

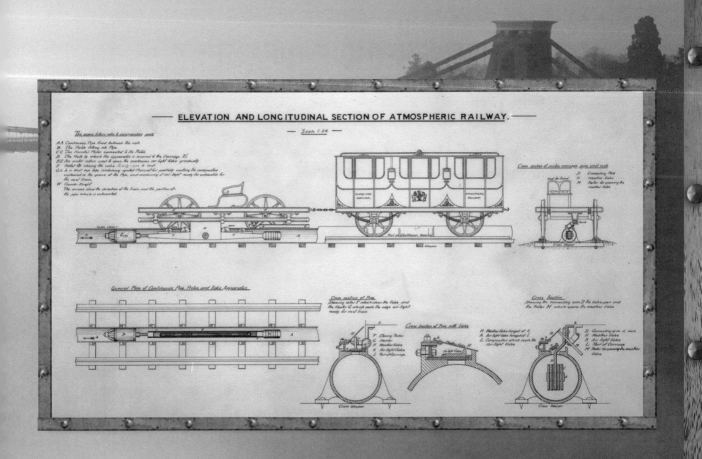

ELEVATION AND LONGITUDINAL SECTION OF ATMOSPHERIC RAILWAY.
— Scale 1:24 —

Brunel constructed 20 miles of track and pipe and lined the railway with eight pumping stations. When it opened in 1847 thousands of spectators turned up to watch his latest miracle in action.

Unfortunately, however, the construction of the Devon Atmospheric Railway was fatally flawed. The slit along the pipe was 2.5 inches wide and covered by a leather flap. The sea air corroded the leather, letting in water and dirt so the vacuum was hard to maintain. When the leather was treated with a sealant to make it weather-proof, the sealant attracted rats, who found it rather tasty!

The other major problem was the pumping stations, which were designed to work with a 15-inch pipe, rather than the 15-inch one which had been used . Both these factors meant that the pumping stations used almost three times more power than Brunel expected and the running costs were significantly higher than the original locomotive-hauled railway. To fix the problems would have cost even more. So, with profits and the line itself being eaten away, the world's longest atmospheric railway closed, only a year after it went into full operation. It was Brunel's biggest failure but, ever the gentleman, he didn't charge a fee for his work.

WHAT IT WILL
LOOK LIKE
AS A PLANE

JEM'S ATMOSPHERIC EXPERIMENT

TV presenter Jem Stansfield decided to demonstrate the principles of an atmospheric railway. He used:

· Four budget vacuum cleaners
· A 30-foot length of tubing, wide enough to fit a human
· A plug for the top of the tubing through which the suction tubes of the vacuum cleaners could go
· A polystyrene piston shaved to fit inside the tubing
· A handlebar to attach to the piston

Jem rigged up 30 feet of scaffolding, to which he attached one end of the tubing and the four vacuum cleaners. He made sure that the polystyrene piston fitted snugly inside the tube but could move easily up and down. Finally he attached the handlebar firmly to the piston so it was strong enough to take his weight.

Then it was time for the moment of truth. The vacuum cleaners were turned on and Jem disappeared up the tubing at a slow and steady rate. The vacuum cleaners were sucking 1/5 of the air out of the space above him, causing low pressure and enough force to pull him up. Luckily he had made sure someone else was there to turn the vacuum cleaners off!

Jem's verdict: "I'd say the vacuum railway was abandoned a little too early. It really works!"

PS. Even if you have four vacuum cleaners, don't try this at home!

POSITIO
OF F'L

Vacuum-zooming canisters

One hundred and fifty years on from Brunel's failed experiment you can still see the atmospheric railway science working in Bristol. The pneumatic tube system at Bristol Royal Infirmary uses a vacuum effect to take canisters along a network of pipes running from building to building around the hospital. Some buildings are half a mile apart so it is invaluable to take tests, records and drugs from place to place. Each canister has an inbuilt computer chip and a central control system oversees each journey. The system is just like a mini underground rail network, with its own zones and stations. It even has a rush hour! In one year, those little canisters make about 200,000 trips.

Nigel Philips from the Bristol Royal Infirmary says, "Brunel himself actually developed a construction technique that was used to build part of the hospital in the 1800s, so I'm delighted that we're keeping a couple of his innovations going. I think we owe a lot of the world that we take for granted to people like him."

The Aeromovel railway

AND… in Porto Alegre in Southern Brazil, Oskar Coester is trying to realise the dreams of Brunel. His "Aeromovel" system uses the same principles as Brunel's atmospheric railway. The system has 1.2km of elevated track that winds between tall buildings and through parks. It is capable of up to 80kmph and uses only a third of the energy of a bus. At present the system consists of just a prototype track with a station at each end, which is used to demonstrate and test the system.

However, Coester has also built a fully functional line in a theme park in Jakarta, Indonesia, which has carried more than three million passengers in the past decade. Coester also hopes that the atmospheric system, with its environmental and economic benefits will soon be adopted by city planners around the world. So it seems that even Isambard Kingdom Brunel's atmospheric failure could still become a success in the end!

The Truth Is Out There, or so they say. Truth is, I've always fancied having my own flying saucer – it'd be just the job with a flying cup of tea and flying biccies, wouldn't it? So let's have a look at some forms of transport which are truly Out Of This World...

FLYING SAUCERS

Are flying saucers just
a figment of over-active
imaginations, or the shape
of things to come?

There have been countless
reports of sightings of
unidentified flying objects (UFOs)
in our skies for centuries – dating
back to the Middle Ages in fact. In the
days before scientists started
explaining what these UFOs were, people
could have mistaken meteors, weird cloud
formations or mirages as alien spaceships
sent to spy on us. However, the public's
obsession really kicked in after American
pilot Kenneth Arnold claimed to have seen nine
'pie plate' shaped objects flying in a chain over
Washington in 1947. The newspapers were quick
to coin the phrase 'flying saucers' and there have
been thousands of recorded sightings since.

British Rail's flying saucer

Ambitious inventors have attempted to design and build their own flying saucers. Many curious designs have been patented, but one in particular stands out – the one registered by British Rail in 1973 for a nuclear-powered 'lifting platform'. The designs looked suspiciously extraterrestrial.

So what was the nationalised railway company doing registering a patent for a flying saucer, at a time when they should have been concerned with the congestion at Crewe or their antiquated rolling stock? Well, it was all down to one of their employees, physicist and engineer Charles Osmond Frederick, and it all came about because of a close encounter.

Charles Frederick says, "I had seen a light in the sky, which got me thinking about flying saucers. It was such an attractive concept that I found it very difficult to think about anything else. I came to the conclusion that you could design a vehicle that would carry passengers."

Frederick's thoughts turned to the problem of powering his spacecraft. NASA's rockets needed an enormous amount of fuel to power them. But Frederick knew of one process that generated huge amounts of energy from very little 'fuel'. That process was called nuclear fusion and it fascinated many physicists at that time.

WHAT IS NUCLEAR FUSION?

Nuclear fusion is what powers our sun. Its light and warmth are the result of the nuclei of hydrogen atoms constantly colliding and fusing together to form heavier helium atoms. This reaction releases huge amounts of energy. Scientists can cause this nuclear reaction in a lab, by forcing atomic nuclei together. The energy released is far larger than the energy needed to ignite the reaction. Now scientists are trying to figure out ways to control the reaction to give us a cheaper, green energy source.

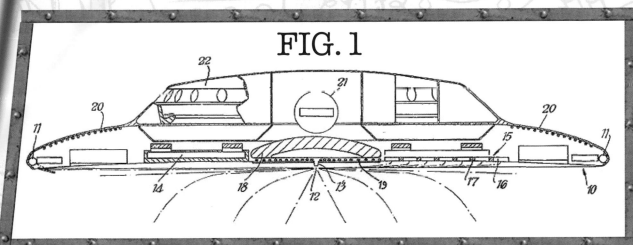

FIG. 1

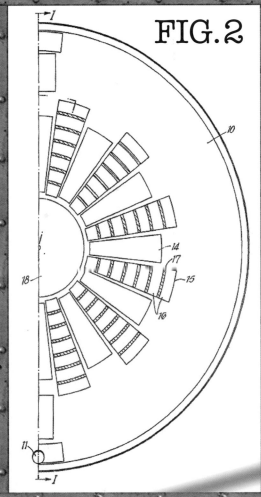

FIG. 2

Frederick's idea was to power his flying saucer by using laser beams to ignite a thermonuclear fusion reaction. This was somewhat removed from his usual field of expertise, which was examining stress levels in train tracks, but British Rail saw potential in Frederick's idea at the time.

It is incredible now to think that the bosses at British Rail would have been interested in such a seemingly far-fetched idea from an employee. After all, it was concerned with space travel rather than train travel, but they were not only interested, they registered a patent on Frederick's behalf.

Beamed energy propulsion

Sadly for the long-suffering commuters of Britain, Frederick's nuclear fusion flying saucer never got off the ground, but a few decades on, it turns out that his idea may not have been so far-fetched after all.

Half way around the world, in a military compound in Brazil, Professor Liek Myrabo and his team of scientists are developing a new technology called 'beamed energy propulsion'. Their aim is to develop a global transportation system enabling people to fly anywhere in the world in just 45 minutes. The theory is not a million miles away from Frederick's.

The professor has been working on his light craft since 1987. Initially funded by NASA, Myrabo developed a prototype flying saucer using lasers for ignition.

The miniature light craft might look like a designer lemon squeezer, but the shape is crucial to the way it works. A powerful laser is beamed at a point in the underside of the craft. This heats the air underneath to 30,000 degrees (hotter than the sun!), which effectively melts the air, causing an atomic reaction. The resulting explosion propels the craft upwards. Using this method, a spacecraft doesn't need any fuel, making it very efficient and cost-effective. It is a system powered by light and air.

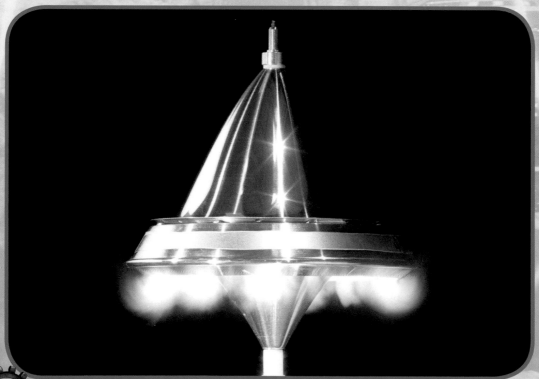

Professor Myrabo's laser-propelled lightcraft.

LASER actually means **L**ight **A**mplification by **S**timulated **E**mission of **R**adiation

Today, Professor Myrabo has scaled up his operation, thanks to a $2.25 million grant from the US government, coupled with collaboration from the Brazilian military, who are in the early stages of their first ever space programme and are hoping to benefit from this new technology. They have built a facility for the sole purpose of researching laser propulsion and now Professor Myrabo is testing his lightcraft to destruction inside a sealed unit at 10 times the speed of sound.

The next stage is to build a full-scale model. Professor Myrabo believes that a manned flight will be possible by 2015, and a fully operational transportation system by 2050. Passengers will just need to purchase a ticket, jump into the pod and be on the other side of the world in 45 minutes, all for the cost of a transatlantic airline ticket today.

Meanwhile, just a break-neck 45 minutes away across the Atlantic in Derbyshire, Charles Osmond Frederick, having invented the future reflects on the one possible flaw in high-speed flying saucer travel. He says, "It's important that the thrust doesn't kill the passengers, but it is certainly an interesting idea and I'm glad we planted it."

Chapter 03
NATURE KNOWS BEST

"Necessity is the Mother of Invention, or so some bright spark once said. Well – not necessarily! In this chapter we'll be looking at inventions inspired by another mother altogether – Mother Nature.

"And Mother Nature doesn't just inspire us, she can provide an eco-friendly source of power too. In fact, Gromit and I have been working on a new form of green energy – or should I say 'greens energy', eh lad? – which I'll be telling you a bit more about later on.

"But first, we'll be finding out about a clock that thinks it's a venus fly-trap, meeting some flying penguins and taking a lesson in architecture from the humble termite."

ROBOTS INSPIRED BY NATURE

Here are some inventions inspired by nature, but if you ask me, they look a bit fishy...

Human beings have used nature to their own advantage for thousands of years – burning wood for warmth, getting food from plants and animals, generating power from wind and water, for example. However, it is only recently that we have looked at ways to adapt nature's secrets for our own purposes. It makes sense when you think that, through evolution, nature has spent billions of years honing form and function, creating creatures that are efficient and perfectly adapted to their environments.

Take aerodynamics, for example. The most streamlined forms on the planet can all be found in the natural world – just look at the way birds fly through the air. Many of the best aerodynamic designs that humans have come up with take their inspiration from nature. The same can be said for underwater dynamics. Fish are sleek, streamlined and incredibly hydrodynamic, they move through the water with grace and ease, so why not base inventions for underwater transport on them?

Manta ray motion

It's the natural world that has inspired a team of German scientists at Festo, an automation and pneumatics company. Markus Fischer is in charge of the bionics team that looks at energy efficient movement in air and in water, hoping to learn lessons that can be put to practical use in industry. The team decided to concentrate on one of the most well-adapted examples in nature – the manta ray.

Manta rays manage to 'fly' through water very efficiently. The up and down motion of their fins is like the flapping of a bird's wings in the air, and the movement is very energy efficient. They can also swim along the seabed without disturbing it and can manoeuvre very easily. The team began to study the movements of the manta ray to learn its secrets. They discovered that the efficiency of movement was due to the structure of its fin, so they decided to replicate it.

A Manta ray 'flying' through the water.

Main pic: The Air Ray in flight from above.

Inset: Controlling the Air Ray takes two pairs of hands!

The Air Ray

The result of the team's work looking at the manta ray is an amazing remote-controlled flying fish called the Air Ray, which moves through the air efficiently and independently. The Air Ray comprises an aluminium-vaporised 'foil' balloon filled with helium and a robotic flapping-wing drive mechanism that has been named the Fin Ray. The structure of the Fin Ray is like a fish fin, with two bones interlinked with cartilage. As a fish pulls its fin through the water, the fin bends in the direction of the force, making it very energy efficient. But the development team went one step further. They added a twisting movement so the Air Ray can also fly backwards or turn on a point.

So, while the Air Ray is just a mechanical skeleton with batteries and motors on the inside, when fully assembled and operational, it is an awesome sight. In flight, the Air Ray is every bit as beautiful, graceful and efficient as a manta ray in water, and incredibly agile.

Gripping fins

The company also looked for a more practical use for the Fin Ray structure. The engineers realised that the flexibility and strength of the structure would make it ideal for use as a gripping tool. By using the principles learnt from the ways a fish's fin moves, Festo have created a strong and incredibly flexible tool that could be used for a number of purposes, including in automated machinery.

The fin gripper system in close-up, showing that it can adapt to any shape. Each internal 'strut' flexes according to the pressure applied to it.

The Air Ray in flight.

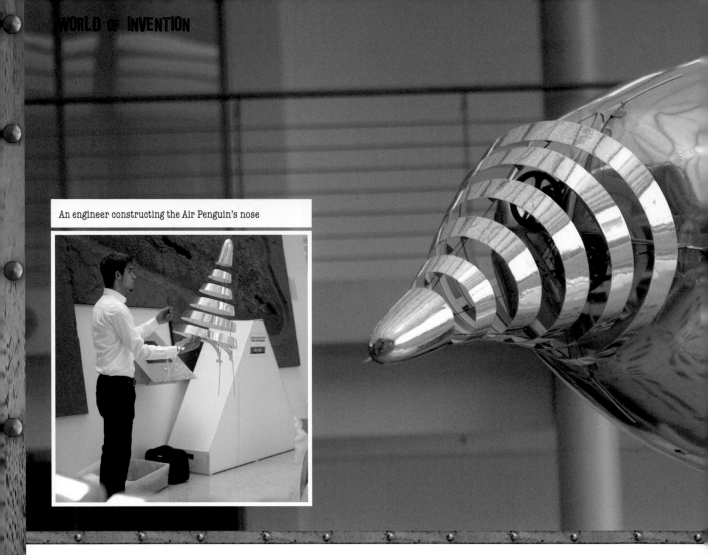

An engineer constructing the Air Penguin's nose

Air Penguins

The development did not stop there. The bionics team took the Fin Ray structure and adapted it to form the nose of another amazing creation – the Air Penguin.

Penguins are fascinating creatures that lost their ability to fly as they evolved over millions of years to become marine birds. They move slowly on land, but in water are amazingly hydrodynamic and swim with ease and grace. The team at Festo have created artificial penguins that fly in the air in a similar way to the real birds swimming in the sea.

The Air Penguin is an autonomously flying object that is made of a helium-filled ballonett (an air-filled container or air bag), which has a capacity of around 1 cubic metre. At each end of the ballonett is a Fin Ray structure that can move in any direction.

The nose and tail of the Air Penguin move in every direction so it can move with the same agility and manoeuvrability as its natural counterpart. The small flapping wings help to make the Penguin rise and descend as it flies through the air.

An Air Penguin in flight.

To see a group of Air Penguins flying is quite amazing. They each have complex navigation and communication systems so they can move freely, exchange information, recognise each other and never collide. This is achieved by the air space being a controlled environment, monitored by invisible ultrasound 'transmitting stations'. A microcontroller allows them to explore this space independently. They can also fly in synchronisation as a group.

Attaching the nose to the body of the Air Penguin.

Aqua Penguins

Festo have also built Aqua Penguins, which are robots that swim just like real penguins – or even better. They use the hydrodynamic contours of the real birds to allow the robots to turn in small spaces, turn on the spot and even swim backwards – which the real birds can't do!

These amazing robots are all part of a programme aimed at using nature as an inspiration – and it's very likely that they will inform machinery, transport and other inventions of the future. Perhaps in a few years' time we'll all be flying around in our own Air Penguins!

"We build things like the Air Ray and the Air Penguin to inspire young people to learn from nature. We learn ourselves from nature and can come up with new solutions in the field of engineering." Markus Fischer.

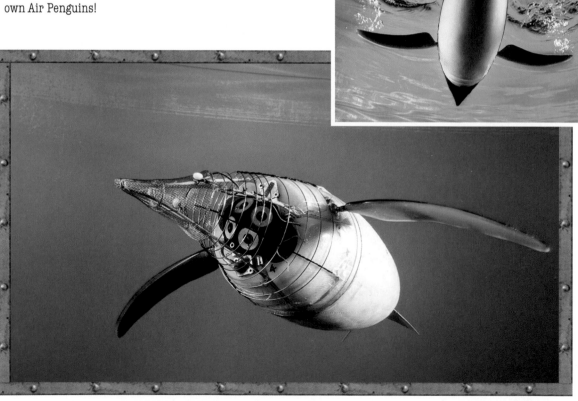

Pollution-detecting robot fish

This amazing-looking robot fish was created by Professor Huosheng Hu and his robotics team at the University of Essex with the aim of detecting pollution in water. It rivals some of its real-life counterparts for beauty, grace and intuitiveness. It has in-built sensors and a sophisticated navigation system that allows it to swim without bumping into things. The swimming motion is like a carp, using side-to-side body movement to propel it through the water in a very energy-efficient way. The more energy-efficient the robots are, the longer they will be able to work without recharging.

Inside the fish are chemical sensors, which detect pollution. The fish will soon be swimming around a busy port in northern Spain collecting data and transmitting information back to a control centre. And if you're wondering if a hungry shark might be tempted to have one for his tea, experiments at the London Aquarium saw the sharks giving the fish a wide berth, probably because of the electromagnetic energy they give off. It seems that sharks are clever enough to know that a robotic fish wouldn't be very tasty!

As I was saying, nature isn't just the inspiration for some inventions, she can power them too. A couple of young boffins have found a way to turn the humble house fly into a source of electricity which can power lamps, robots and even clocks. Must be what they mean when they say 'Time flies', eh Gromit?

CARNIVOROUS ROBOTS

Whenever robots are invented to do jobs for humankind, they usually need external energy of some kind to power them. Unless there is a supply of electricity, oil or other fuels, your robots are unlikely to carry on working. This can cause difficulties in areas where fuel supplies are not plentiful or immediately at hand. It also causes problems when we want to cut down on the use of fossil fuels and be kinder to the environment.

Because of this issue, inventors are now coming up with robots that are self-sustaining; that can feed themselves with energy.

For instance, imagine having a lamp in your house that runs not on mains electricity but on flies. That's right, flies! The lamp shown below is actually a fly-eating robot! It works in a similar way to a carnivorous plant such as a pitcher plant. These plants use bright colours or nectar to attract flies and other insects to them. They then trap and digest the insects inside, getting a ready supply of food. The design team who came up with the idea for the lamp, James Auger and Jimmy Loizeau, say it is not just functional; it is also entertaining – far more interesting and intriguing than watching sticky flypaper anyway!

A pitcher plant.

The carnivorous lamp.

Ecobots

The lamp was inspired by a series of clever robots called "ecobots" developed by the Bristol Robotics Lab. The aim is to create self-sufficient robots capable of powering themselves by extracting energy from their surroundings. At the heart of these ecobots is a new technology called the microbial fuel cell. This cell is 'fed' by organic matter – anything from fruit to dead insects – and it uses chemicals inside the cell to 'digest' the matter and extract the particles it needs (electrons) to create electricity.

With the fly-eating lamp, the flies, as well as moths and other insects, are attracted by the light. They crawl in through holes but then can't crawl out again. When they die, they fall into the microbial fuel cell and the cell turns them into electricity, which lights the ultraviolet lamp. In turn, the light attracts more flies. The result – a completely self-supporting robot that can survive without any human intervention.

But Auger and Loizeau didn't stop at lamps – they've designed a flypaper robotic clock, a fly-stealing robot and a mouse-eating coffee table too!

The flypaper robotic clock

This clock uses a long, slow-moving strip of sticky flypaper to catch flies. It then scrapes the flies off the paper and into a microbial fuel cell, which 'digests' them in the same way as the lamp does. The energy generated powers a small digital clock and the motor to turn the flypaper.

Detail of the flypaper robotic clock, showing a dead fly stuck to the flypaper and about to drop into the fuel cell.

The fly-stealing robot

This robot mimics the symbiosis found in the natural world where different species learn to co-exist with each other. In this case, a robot and a spider help one another. The robot provides a safe and secure place for the spider to spin its web, but in return the robot steals some of the spider's flies to feed itself, using a camera to track the fly and a robotic arm to grab it.

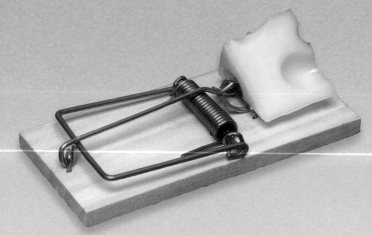

Next-generation ecobots

The day that robots can completely fend for themselves is some way off – they still need people to set them up and switch them on. And for a robot to be truly autonomous, they will need to search for, collect and digest food in the same way as living organisms. This dream is still very much alive at the Bristol Robotics Lab. They are hoping that their next generation eco-bots will be able to run on waste water and even generate their own water. The hope is to create 'release and forget' robots that could have multiple uses, from pollution monitoring to underwater exploration to waste reduction.

The mousetrap table

Mice can be a real problem when they come to live in your home, eating your food and generally scaring the life out of you when they unexpectedly run across your kitchen floor. Many people put down traps to catch them, but with this coffee table in their home they wouldn't have to.

One leg of the table has a hole in it, like a tunnel, big enough for mice to scamper up. The hole starts down at the floor and the mice, attracted to leftover crumbs on the table, run up the leg. When they get to the top they trip a sensor that opens a trap door. The mice then plunge to their doom and the table, quite literally, gobbles them up, turning all their electrons into power to run the sensor, the trap door and a little digital clock on the side – mouse problem solved and free power into the bargain!

James Auger says, "Some people have 'issues' with the idea of a mouse-eating robot. And in a way, that's what we want. As well as being functional and aesthetically pleasing, these robots are intended to provoke debate about the future of robot autonomy."

The mousetrap table.

WALLACE'S TOP 5 INVENTIONS
INSPIRED BY NATURE

1. All aboard the Number Seventeen Jumbo!
This artificial elephant comes with built-in seats –
a lot more fun than travelling on a bendy bus,
and less dung than your regular elephant too!

As an animal-lover myself, it makes me proud to see inventors taking their cue from the natural world. But in some cases, their contraptions are neither fish nor fowl...

2. This poor little chap had wheels fitted when his back legs became too painful to walk – and they knitted him a smart jumper to go with them – how do you fancy one of those, eh Gromit?

3. Sleek, sophisticated, stylish – you might think this car was designed for a James Bond film. But in fact it's based on the humble box fish. I wonder if it can go underwater too?

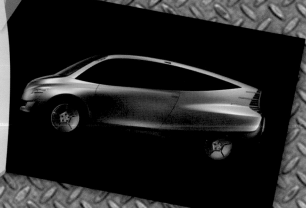

4. You can really get into the swim of things with this natty new swimsuit, which is designed to mimic shark skin, allowing you to glide through the water with ease. Beats the doggy paddle, eh Gromit?

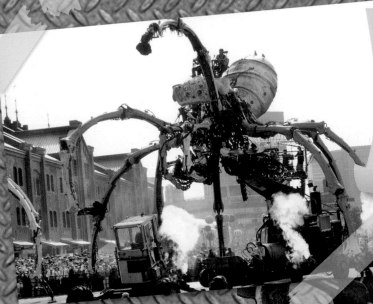

5. No, this isn't a creature from a 1950s B movie, it's a spider-inspired art installation which can even shoot steam out of its backside. Well, if you weren't scared of spiders before, you will be now!

83

FEATURED INVENTOR

You know I said Gromit and I were working on 'greens' energy? Well, I can take the wraps off our latest top-secret project just for you. His name is Kevin – our Jumbo-Generator. He takes in a barrow-load of sprouts at one end, and after a few moments' digestion, he can produce enough natural gas to power the entire studio. The ultimate in wind-power, you might say!

And speaking of wind, here's a man who uses it to rather more artistic ends: our featured inventor...

THEO JANSEN and the STRANDBEESTS

Theo Jansen probably would not call himself an inventor. He studied physics at the University of Delft, in the Netherlands before becoming a painter. After several years as an artist he decided to branch out and become what might be called a 'creator', bringing together the worlds of science and art.

For more than 20 years now Theo has been creating and adapting moving sculptures that he calls strandbeests. They crawl along the beach independently, looking like alien invaders straight out of War of the Worlds. But Jansen's creations are not creatures made of proteins and fuelled by food like other life forms. Nor are they robots made of metal and programmed by humans. They are simply made of yellow plastic tubes and they get their energy from the wind.

The versatility of yellow plastic tubing

Jansen loves yellow plastic tubing. He makes lots of things out of it and says it is incredibly versatile. It is flexible so you can bend it into any shape you like, but it becomes extremely rigid in a triangular construction. It is also hollow, so you can run pistons and spokes through it and you can store air in it, too. These things are hugely important to Jansen and his work.

He first used plastic tubing in 1979 when he built a flying saucer. It was four metres wide and filled with helium. He flew it over the city of Delft in the Netherlands, causing pandemonium and attracting considerable attention! Since then, the physicist turned artist, has been working on his strandbeests and now has a herd of different species.

Theo Jansen standing next to his latest strandbeest on the shore in the Netherlands.

The idea for the strandbeests came about by accident. Theo Jansen explains:

"The strategy I followed to assemble the animals is the complete opposite of that taken by an engineer.

"Suppose that engineers at a university of technology were to be commissioned to make something that could move of its own volition along the beach. What would you expect them to do? You can bet your life they would be ready in three months and also that they would have assembled stainless steel robot-like devices armed with sensors, cameras and light cells. Devices that are first thought out and then assembled. That's how engineers work…First they pore over books, then they open all the drawers in their workplace and take out what they need. It's a working method that gives rapid and reliable results, no two ways about it.

"Countermanding that is the fact that any such devices engineers at these universities would develop would all be much alike. This is because our brains are much alike. We think we have exceptional brains (and of course we do) but they are embarrassingly alike in many ways. Everything we think up can, in principle, be thought up by someone else. Now real ideas, as evolution shows us, occur by sheer chance. The idea for the beach animals was one such accident. It came about after I had been fooling around with plastic tubes for quite a time. It was the beach animals themselves that let me make them. And the plastic tubing showed me how…"

Theo's new strandbeest, Siamesis, with its sails billowing in the wind.

Evolution of the strandbeests

Jansen built his first walking creature, called *Animaris Vulgaris*, using sticky tape. Unfortunately the poor thing wasn't strong enough to walk so Jansen had to find a solution to the problem. He developed a computer model to help him find the perfect size and shape of the leg. This gave him what he calls '11 holy numbers'. The numbers indicate the necessary ratio of tube lengths to give the perfect walking motion.

Each strandbeest is made up of hundreds of yellow plastic tubes.

After giving his creations the ability to 'walk', Jansen went on to give them 'nerves' and 'senses', so they developed survival instincts. He has given them water feelers – partly made of lemonade bottles – that sense the change in resistance between air and water. If they detect water, a switch turns the animals away from the rising tide. Without it, the animals could be destroyed.

Animaris Percipiere has a storm sensor in its nose, which detects a rise in the wind speeds. If it senses danger, it hammers a peg into the sand so it will not be blown away.

Animaris Currens Ventosa has the ability to capture and store energy. Sails on its back drive pistons (made of plastic tubing, of course), to pump air into lemonade bottles. The animal can use the stored air if it needs to escape from the sea but the wind is not strong enough.

The latest strandbeest is called *Animaris Siamesis*. Siamesis is a twin animal – two animals joined together, holding and supporting each other against strong winds. It also has a large wind stomach that can store air should it need it.

Jansen believes Siamesis is a significant step in the evolution of the strandbeests. He hopes that one day they will become autonomous, intelligent life forms that can live and survive on their own. With every new generation, Jansen's dream moves closer to becoming a reality. And, who knows, over time his strandbeests might also do important work – moving sand to build up the dunes to help protect the flat coastline from rising sea levels. But regardless of whether they develop a 'usefulness', they remain incredible and beautiful creatures with abilities we can only marvel at.

"I can assure you it's not easy being God," says Jansen. "There are plenty of disappointments along the way. But on the few occasions that things work out, being God is the most wonderful thing in the world."

Have you ever dreamed of living underwater? Just think, you'd never have to have a bath again! Here are some inventors who are trying to make that dream come true.

Never Got off the Drawing Board...

LIVING UNDERWATER

About 400 million years ago, primitive life made the monumental journey out of the sea to begin a new chapter in evolution – to live on dry land. Since then, Mother Nature has done a brilliant job adapting all those resulting species to breathe air and we as human beings are now very good at it. Our lungs are expert at filtering out the oxygen our bodies need from the air we breathe and passing it into our blood. They are also efficient at taking out the carbon dioxide we don't need and getting rid of that as we exhale.

Unfortunately for divers, our lungs are not so clever underwater. All those years of evolution have meant that, now, we can only survive un-aided on land. Even though there is oxygen gas dissolved in water, our lungs just can't extract it, so those who want to spend any serious time underwater either have to strap on bulky scuba equipment or hold their breath for a very, very long time!

So how do fish do it? Fish are expert at extracting oxygen from water to survive because they have useful little things called gills. Gills are like a liquid-proof membrane; they allow the oxygen in the water to pass through them. They couldn't really be simpler. But like so many things in nature, when it comes to making an artificial version, it is far from simple. It is a challenge that so far has stumped generations of inventors.

The gills of a tiger shark.

Jacques Cousteau's vision of an underwater community

In the 1960s, the idea of living underwater rivalled the space race for public attention. Building an underwater habitat in which humans could live was just as intriguing and romantic as building a habitable city on the moon. The famous underwater explorer Jacques Cousteau outlined his vision for the future in a speech he made to the British Sub Aqua Club in 1962.

"It will happen," Captain Cousteau said. "Surgery will affix a set of artificial gills to man's circulatory system – right here at the neck – which will permit him to breathe oxygen from the water like a fish. Then the lungs will be by-passed and he will be able to live and breathe in any depth for any amount of time without harm.

"Do you realise what that will mean? He will be able to observe, train, cultivate and exploit the seas at first-hand. Maybe the first man will be an undersea farmer, or miner, or rancher. Maybe just a scientist. At any rate, there will be no depth-time barrier; we know that. When his duties are done, he will be rehabilitated to air breathing by more surgery. It will happen, I promise you."

Top: Jacques Cousteau; bottom: Jacques Cousteau's underwater saucer.

The underwater hamster

Jacques Cousteau inspired inventors such as scientist Walter Robb. In 1962, Robb successfully built a sealed box from an artificial material, which worked just like a gill membrane. It allowed oxygen to pass through the walls of the box when immersed in water. This was good news for the hamster living in the box at the time! Robb's hamster lived to tell the tale after a miraculous 11 days underwater. It wasn't long before other inventors decided to rise to the challenge.

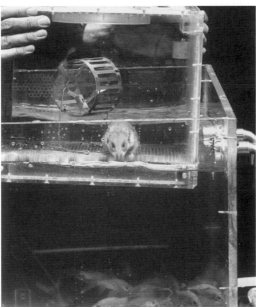

Walter Robb's underwater hamster.

American Waldemar Ayres tested another membrane device, which allowed him to breathe underwater for nearly an hour and a half. He possibly could have stayed down longer if leaky pipes hadn't forced him to surface.

The diving dog

And then there was Edward Cussler, a Professor of Chemical Engineering at Minnesota University. Cussler took a slightly different approach. He tested out his membrane device on his beloved pet dog, Muggins. Cussler must have been very confident that his device would work because he lowered the dog into the Mississippi River inside a metre square box and left him for three hours underwater. Much to Cussler's relief Muggins seemed unharmed by his experience, although he probably never brought Cussler his slippers again!

Despite the success of these inventions, no one had really come up with a device that could turn Jacques Cousteau's vision into reality. The race to conquer space had beaten the race to conquer the oceans in both man's imagination and in reality. It looked as if the dream of living underwater had itself sprung a leak.

Artificial gills

However, one man is working hard to keep the dream alive. Israeli inventor Alan Bodner thinks he may have found the solution – an artificial gill capable of producing enough air from water to allow a human being to breathe safely underwater.

It all started when his seven-year-old son asked him about the difference between humans and fish, and why people need air tanks when underwater.

A 1920s diving suit.

Bodner says, "I knew there was air dissolved in water and that fish breathed this air. I thought, with all the technology in the world, why couldn't we breathe this air too?"

This sparked nine years of research and experiment for Bodner, working in his backyard to try to get his design off the drawing board. He successfully built a working prototype of an artificial gill using a very different method from his predecessors. Bodner knew that water contained only about 0.5% of dissolved air. He also knew that this air contained more oxygen than the air we breathe.

OXYGEN IN WATER

We all know that water is made up of hydrogen and oxygen atoms - H_2O - but it is not this oxygen that fish or humans breathe, because a chemical reaction has bonded the oxygen and hydrogen atoms together to make water molecules – a liquid at normal temperatures.

However, water also contains dissolved air – tiny little bubbles of gas. This dissolved air allows living things to grow and live in water, such as plants and fish. If there is no dissolved air in the water, it is stagnant, and very little can grow.

The dissolved air gets into the water in a number of ways, for example when water is aerated by plunging over a waterfall, or when waves crash on the beach. Oxygen gas is also a waste product of underwater plants when they photosynthesize.

One of the laws to describe how gases behave is called Henry's Law. It describes how the amount of gas dissolved in a liquid is proportional to the amount of pressure of the gas on the liquid. So Bodner used this law to create a system that released the air in water using a high-pressure pump and a centrifuge device –
a high spinning drum, like those fairground rides that pin you to the walls as they spin.

Water is pumped under high pressure along a pipe into a small centrifuge, where it is spun round at high speed. The spinning centrifuge causes a whirlpool. In the centre of that whirlpool the air pressure is much lower (as in the eye of a storm). This low pressure means that air can escape from the water, in the same way as a bottle of fizzy drink releases bubbles when you open the cap. The air is then captured in an air bag so that good old-fashioned human lungs can breathe it in without the need for Cousteau's radical surgery idea.

Bodner says, "The idea of extracting breathable oxygen from water using pressure means that we have an almost limitless air supply. All we need is the power to run our apparatus and a method for expelling CO_2."

Bodner has designed and built a prototype of his system, and it works – as long as there is enough water and power to keep the system going. The one drawback is that the system is not yet portable. For it to be practical for divers, it needs to be small and lightweight but it also needs to be capable of pumping around 200 litres of water through the system every minute to produce enough oxygen to sustain a diver underwater. If Bodner can do that, it could revolutionize scuba diving. Divers could stay down as long as they like without worrying about empty air tanks, although they would, of course, still require energy.

But Bodner isn't sitting around waiting for technology to catch up with him. He is looking at other uses for his system, such as providing air for underwater human habitats. He still has a lot of work to do on his design before we can all pack up and move to the ocean floor but, if he can perfect his invention, the dream of living underwater is one step closer.

He says, "I'm hoping that I can do my part to help us really explore this world – just as fish do."

Jacques Cousteau would surely have approved.

TERMITE HOUSES

Bugs! Nasty little things...
or are they? Perhaps we
can learn a thing or two
from our many-legged
friends. Read on and see...

Until now, termites have not been particularly
popular with architects. Given their tendency to
eat wood, and thus be able to reduce buildings
to rubble in a few days, it's not surprising.
However, it seems that a new wave of architects
and builders is seeking inspiration from the
humble termite. It turns out that the insects
are great builders, who work in harmony with
nature – and they could show us the way
forward when it comes to environmentally-
friendly architecture and construction.

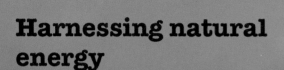

Harnessing natural energy

In hot and humid countries, termite mounds dominate the landscape. These mounds are very complex and are constructed in a way that uses the natural energy of their surroundings. Unlike humans and other creatures, which tend to build structures that separate them from the extremes of their environment, termites actually use that environment to make their surroundings perfect for them to thrive in. No other species is known to engineer its surroundings to quite the same extent.

The insects live in some of the most extreme environments on earth. In sub-Saharan Africa, for example, temperatures can reach 35 degrees C by day, and -14 degrees C at night. A species of termite that lives in this location, *Macrotermes Michaelseni*, has worked out a way of ensuring that its homes are just the right temperature even when the outside air is scorchingly hot or bitingly cold.

The mounds have a form of air-conditioning built into their construction. A series of shafts in the mound all face towards the sun, meaning that they capture the sun's rays. The flow of air is regulated through a network of underground tunnels with very tall chimney-like outlets. This means that air moves freely around the mound.

The bulk of a termite mound is for ventilation, with the main living quarters for the termites around 1.5 metres underground.

The mounds of *Macrotermes Michaelseni* are designed to provide the perfect setting – temperature, humidity and ventilation – for the development of a type of fungus. The termites use this fungus to help digest the wood that they eat and transform it into a more nutrient-rich source of food.

Opposite left: Termite mound exterior;
right: Cross-section of a termite mound.

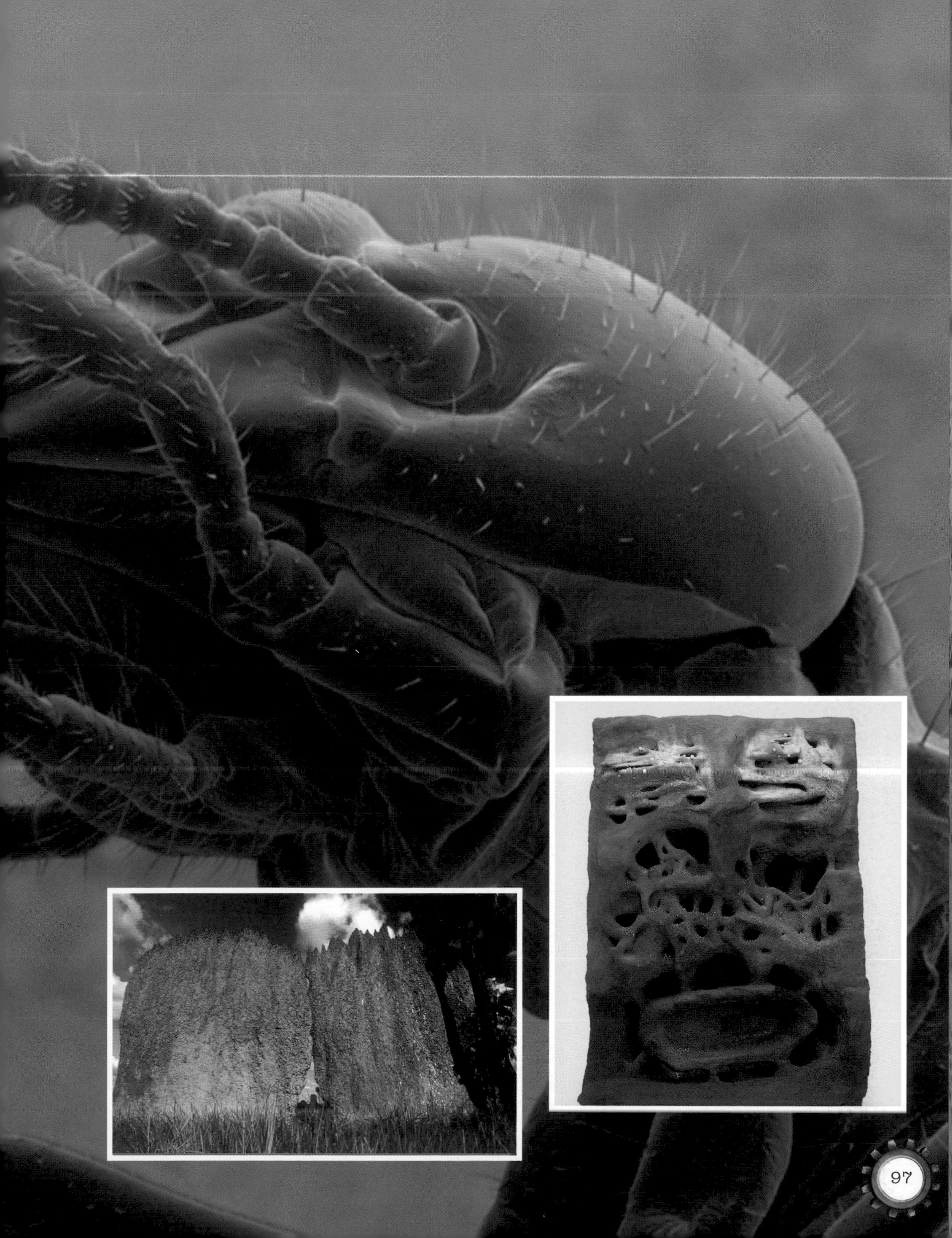

Taking inspiration from termite houses

Termites and their incredible engineering feats are now inspiring inventors and architects in their attempts to tackle some of the biggest issues facing humankind. As natural resources become increasingly scarce, we are having to examine ways of becoming more energy efficient. Buildings and their occupants are heavy users of energy and it is estimated that more than 40% of all the energy used in Europe is wasted by buildings.

Termite mounds manage to function solely using natural energy from the sun, the wind and natural convection currents. What better inspiration for future architects, builders and designers could there be? There is even a term for building and design that is inspired by this form of nature – 'freeform construction'.

Instead of working with nature, traditional buildings tend to use walls as barriers to the outside, separating their occupants from the natural world. Of course, this means that they almost always need artificial ways of circulating air, generating heat or keeping cool. In particular, air-conditioning for buildings in hot countries uses a great amount of energy.

Freeform construction aims to use the environment to enable buildings to 'breathe' naturally rather than being cut off from the outside world. One idea is that walls are constructed to be porous, using a network of tunnels that manage to exchange gases from the outside to the inside and vice versa, using the wind.

The Eastgate shopping centre in Harare was one of the first buildings to take inspiration from termite mounds. The design of this shopping centre is based on the external structure of a termite mound, and it uses only around 10% of the energy of buildings of similar size. Rupert Soar and the team behind the development now believe that they can take inspiration from the insect world to a completely new level. Rupert says, "We used 3-D scanning to try to examine the inside of termite mounds as has never been done before. What we discovered is that the whole structure breathes, almost like a human lung. Now we want to use that knowledge to make buildings that can self-regulate in the same way."

Using freeform construction, Rupert is aiming to combine the lessons learnt from nature with up-to-the-minute technology.

He says, "We can design structures on a computer and then 'print' them in concrete. With the lessons we've learnt from nature, we can create complex structures that make the most of passive energy sources like the wind and the sun, just like termites do. The only limit is the architect's imagination."

Robotic termite architects

And Rupert's plans don't end there. He feels that the next step will be the development of robot termites that can be used *en masse*, hundreds of thousands at a time, to create structures of any size and complexity. Just like the real thing, these robot termites would act like live-in architects, constantly improving and adapting the building to keep it functioning to maximum capability.

Rupert says, "I really believe this is the future of construction. In 25 years I expect the use of this technology to be widespread. And using this theory, we could send armies of robot termites out to colonise other planets."

Top and above: The Eastgate shopping centre in Harare – inspired by termites.

Chapter 04

REACH FOR THE SKY

"When it comes to invention, the sky really is the limit. Ever since man first looked to the stars, he's been dreaming up ways of getting off the ground. Of course, that's nothing new for Gromit and me – we had a Grand Day Out visiting the moon on our very first adventure.

"In this chapter, we'll be looking at some other attempts to get airborne – whether by rocket, or jetpack or even a flying bicycle!

"So turn the page for some inventions which are truly out of this world…"

MARS MISSION SPACESUITS

Of course, every space ship needs a stylish spacesuit to go with it. So let's take a look at what the well-dressed astronaut is wearing this season...

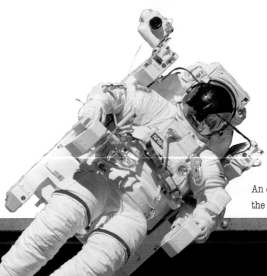

An earlier form of spacesuit -
the Extravehicular Mobility Unit (EMU).

It's in our nature as human beings to wonder what lies beyond our boundaries. We're always looking for new experiences and new discoveries. For example, many of us are keen to know if there is life on other planets or what it would be like to set foot on Mars.

In terms of exploring Mars, the US President, Barack Obama, believes that by the mid 2030s we will be able to send humans to orbit Mars and return them safely to Earth. He sees this as one of the next big steps in space exploration.

The BioSuit

Professor Dava Newman, Professor of Aeronautics and Astronautics at the Massachusetts Institute of Technology, has been working on the BioSuit, a radical new suit that should keep humans alive on Mars.

Professor Newman explains that when astronauts go to Mars, in order to explore the planet to the best of their abilities they will need to do many physical tasks such as hammer rocks, bend down to check soil samples, climb peaks and descend valleys. They will need their full physical capabilities unencumbered by a bulky spacesuit. Ideally the suit that explorers wear on Mars will need to protect them from the harsh environment while still enabling the full range of human movements.

Professor Dava Newman.

103

Second skin

The atmosphere on Mars is very thin and without a suit to simulate the air pressure found on Earth, human blood would boil in its veins. The BioSuit fits like shrinkwrap, squeezing the human body evenly at 4.3lbs per square inch.

The suit acts like a second skin, rather than a sealed mobile Earth environment which existing suits provide. It supplies mechanical pressure by means of strong elastic garments, as opposed to the previous suits that pressurise the suit with gas.

The red lines on the suit follow the major muscle groups, allowing full flexibility and mobility. The black lines are where smart materials will be placed. These materials will enable thermal control, so that the astronauts can heat themselves up or cool themselves down, as well as taking physiological measurements, such as heart rate, to ensure that the person inside the suit remains healthy.

Left: Professor Dava Newman in the BioSuit;
Above: Close up of the BioSuit.

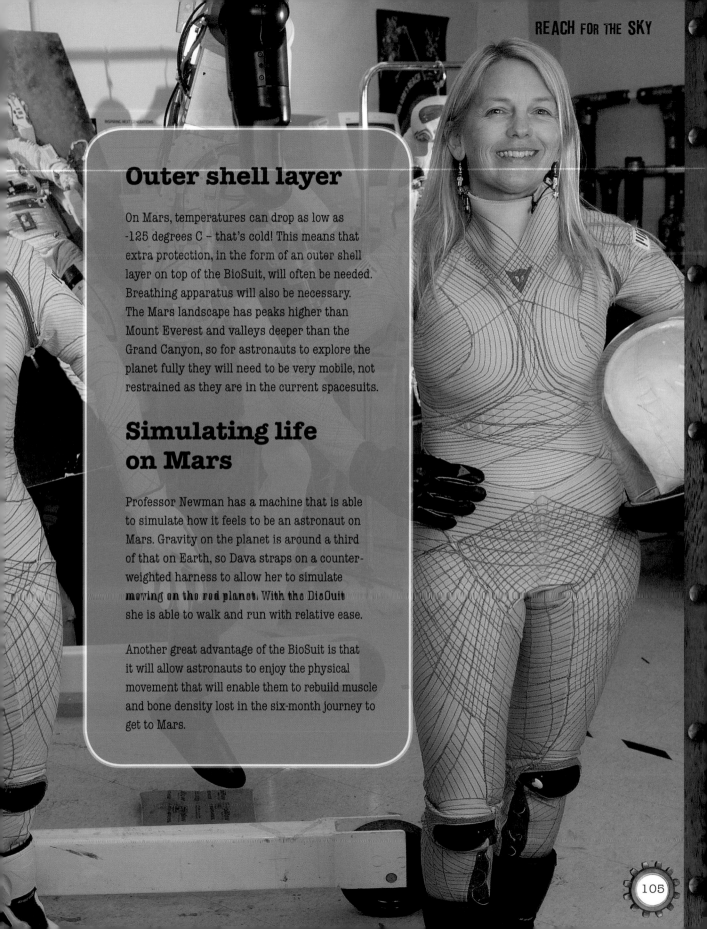

Outer shell layer

On Mars, temperatures can drop as low as
-125 degrees C – that's cold! This means that
extra protection, in the form of an outer shell
layer on top of the BioSuit, will often be needed.
Breathing apparatus will also be necessary.
The Mars landscape has peaks higher than
Mount Everest and valleys deeper than the
Grand Canyon, so for astronauts to explore the
planet fully they will need to be very mobile, not
restrained as they are in the current spacesuits.

Simulating life on Mars

Professor Newman has a machine that is able
to simulate how it feels to be an astronaut on
Mars. Gravity on the planet is around a third
of that on Earth, so Dava straps on a counter-
weighted harness to allow her to simulate
moving on the red planet. With the BioSuit
she is able to walk and run with relative ease.

Another great advantage of the BioSuit is that
it will allow astronauts to enjoy the physical
movement that will enable them to rebuild muscle
and bone density lost in the six-month journey to
get to Mars.

Did you know that the earliest space pioneers were plucky little space pooches? They had their own dog-shaped space suits too. Fancy yourself in one of those, eh Gromit?

From space dogs to BioSuits

The BioSuit is the result of six decades of space-suit design that started with those worn by the famous space dogs of the Soviet Union. Right now, the BioSuit is only a concept design, but when we finally take our first steps on Mars it is likely to be in a suit pioneered by the remarkable Professor Newman.

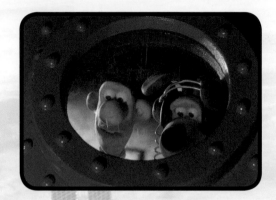

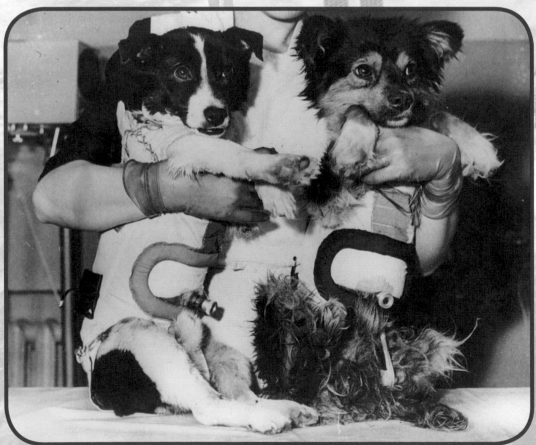

Russian space dogs, 1966.

MARS FACTS

- Mars has the largest volcano in the solar system (Olympus Mons, a huge 27km high and 600km across). Earth's largest volcano is on Hawaii and is only 9km high.

- There are deep canyons, volcanic mountains and craters formed by meteorite impact. Some areas are littered with boulders; others are covered in sand dunes.

- The temperature on Mars varies depending on surface location and altitude. The atmosphere is coldest at high altitudes where typical temperatures are below -200 degrees F (-125 degrees C).

- The average annual temperature on Mars is cold, about -81 degrees F (-62 degrees C). However, the temperature on the planet may reach a high of about 70 degrees F (20 degrees C) at noon, at the equator in the summer.

- The temperature drops dramatically only a short distance above the surface of Mars in the daytime. If you stood on the surface in the daytime, your head would be colder than your feet.

- Mars has two moons, named Phobos (meaning 'fear') and Deimos (meaning 'dread').

- The recent discovery that Mars probably had liquid water on its surface many centuries ago means that the conditions for life may have existed at some time on the planet. If any life exists on Mars today, scientists think it is most likely to be in water chambers beneath the Martian surface. These underground chambers could hold microscopic organisms called extremophiles, organisms that evolved strategies for existing in extreme environments.

HOME-MADE ROCKETS

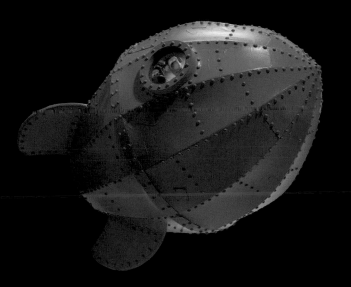

My own home-made rocket has proved quite an inspiration for many other inventors, though I do say so myself. Just take a look at these...

You've heard of Houston, Cape Canaveral and the Kennedy Space Center – places that are synonymous with the dream of conquering space. Well now there is another name that can stand proudly alongside them – Duckinfield in Manchester. Nestling on a quiet industrial estate in this town is the factory of Britain's answer to NASA – former lab technician turned rocket scientist, Steve Bennett.

Steve was five when he fell in love with rockets and started trying to making his own at the age of 13, but it wasn't until much later that he left his job to start building them for real.

Steve Bennett, rocket scientist.

Taking tourists into space

Steve started his company, Starchaser, in 1992 and, since then, he and his team have built and successfully launched seven rockets. They are now working towards their eighth. Steve's dream is that his organisation becomes the world's first independent company to launch tourists into space and return them safely to Earth.

Steve has stiff competition, such as Virgin boss Richard Branson who also wants to introduce a service to take customers into space, but Steve believes he is ahead of his rivals. His rocket, the 23m long Nova II, may look every bit a classic rocket, but it has kept up with the green revolution. Rocket fuel is expensive stuff so Bennett has made the Nova II a hybrid running on liquid oxygen and solid fuel made of old car tyres.

Steve says, "Yes, it is ridiculously expensive. Yes, it is complex and hugely ambitious. The odds are definitely against me, but that's what dreams are for. And if it was easy, it wouldn't be worth doing.

One of Starchaser's
test rockets, Skybolt

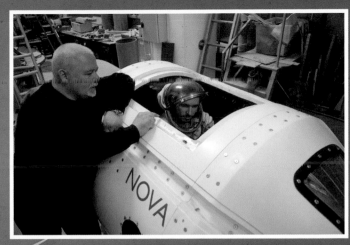

Steve and project co-ordinator, Matthew Shewbridge, in the Nova II capsule.

"We've sold two seats on our first flight already at £250,000 each. Both my passengers have insisted that I pilot the rocket myself, so obviously I'm pretty keen that we all come back in one piece!"

The launch will be in New Mexico and the aim is for Nova II to reach a height of 100km into space. Those on board will experience about 5g (five times the force of gravity) and about 10 minutes of weightlessness before the capsule returns home by parachute.

Steve remarks, "A lot of people think I'm mad for trying this, but when you look at the history of space flight, I'm just following in the footsteps of the real pioneers like Robert Goddard."

limit

EARTH

THE FORCES OF GRAVITY

Without gravity, we would all be flying off into space without a rocket. In a nutshell, gravity is what gives weight to objects and causes them to fall when dropped. The Earth (and every planet) creates its own gravitational field, which exerts a force on all objects on its surface.

Gravity is what keeps us grounded. If the ground fell away we'd fall farther because we are being pulled into the centre of the Earth the whole time. So for a rocket to get out of the Earth's atmosphere it needs to break through this gravitational pull by accelerating fast. For passengers in the rocket, this acceleration causes g-forces far greater than they are used to. This could cause dizziness, loss of vision or they may even pass out. However, when they get farther away from Earth the gravitational pull gets less and less until they feel so light they can float around like a bubble.

Robert Goddard.

Robert Goddard

American Robert Goddard was one of the earliest pioneers of rocket flight. Back in 1926, when the idea of going to the moon was still a fantasy, Goddard became the first man in history to launch a liquid-fuelled rocket.

Goddard and his team launched more than 30 rockets over 15 years, reportedly achieving altitudes as high as 2.6km and going as fast as 885km/h.

He was ridiculed at the time, but his ideas on space flight turned out to inspire the generation who went on to create the modern space age.

113

WALLACE'S TOP 5 FLYING (OR NOT-SO FLYING) INVENTIONS

1. This chap is taking to the air like a duck to water – and I've got a nasty suspicion that's where he's going to end up – in the water!

Of course, what goes up must come down – and here are a few aviation experts who ended up having quite a bumpy landing...

2. I'm not sure that dressing up as a knight improves your chances of getting airborne. This fellow has just taken a long walk off a short pier – d'you think he was dragon his feet, eh lad?

3. Of course, it's important to look your best when you're going to fly. Maybe this smart gent is hoping to get an upgrade to First Class!

4. This flying machine has got a pretty impressive wingspan – it'd put an albatross to shame. Unfortunately, it turned out to be a bit of an albatross as a flying machine too.

5. Oho! A flying platform – what a great way to dust the top shelf! The only trouble is, it seems to be making more dust than you'd be able to clean off in the first place...

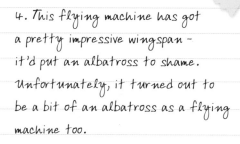

JETPACKS

Take a look at these, Gromit. They'll blow you away!

Jetpacks are the stuff of childhood dreams. Seeing Buck Rogers, James Bond and Star Wars' bounty hunter, Boba Fett fly jetpacks made generations of us fantasize that we might all have such contraptions in the future. We could slip it on, buckle up, and instantly be up in the air and able to go wherever we wanted to go. For some boys that dream stayed with them into adulthood, and now they are turning their dreams into reality.

A demonstration of the Bell Rocket Belt.

Jetpacks in space

If you are an astronaut in space, flying a jetpack is a sensible way to get from A to B. Because of the lack of gravity in space, a jetpack is easy to control; all you need is a tiny bit of power to go a long way.

The first examples were called Manned Manoeuvring Units (MMUs), powered by compressed nitrogen gas. Their introduction meant that astronauts could leave the spacecraft without being tethered. They were independent and could control their own movements.

MMUs have now been replaced by the SAFER, a smaller, simpler version of the MMU.

Jetpacks on Earth

Back down on planet Earth, jetpacks are not so practical. They have to fight against the pull of gravity – it takes a huge amount of thrust to lift man and machine into the air. But people have been trying for decades to make jetpacks a possibility, for both military and recreational purposes.

Skystormer

Designs for jetpacks date back to the Second World War. Late into the war, the Germans made a device called the 'Himmelstürmer', or Skystormer in English. The Skystormer was designed to enable engineers to jump across

A Manned Manoeuvring Unit (MMU) in use.

enemy defences, such as minefields and barbed wire obstacles, or to cross rivers if bridges had been destroyed. The Skystormer comprised two Schmidt pulse jet tubes mounted on the wearer's body – the tube on the wearer's back was high-powered and angled to create lift and forward motion. The tube on the wearer's chest produced less thrust but gave the wearer greater control. With both tubes ignited, and fed by oxygen from a separate tank, the wearer could take long leaps of up to 60 metres.

Project Grasshopper

In 1958, two German engineers created another 'jump belt' and called their work Project Grasshopper. The thrust was generated by high-pressure compressed nitrogen that was released through small nozzles causing upward thrust – so much thrust that the wearer could rise up to 7 metres. If the wearer leaned forward they could 'run' at a speed of up to 45 to 50 km/h. The engineers then tried a jump belt fuelled by hydrogen peroxide. The demonstrations were successful but there was no funding, so Project Grasshopper ended.

The Bell Rocketbelt

Meanwhile, in America, the US army were looking at jetpacks too. They funded a project called the Bell Rocketbelt, undertaken by a company called Bell Aerospace. The Bell Rocketbelt worked in a similar way to the German belt – releasing compressed nitrogen gas through small nozzles to generate upward thrust. And in 1961, a week after Yuri Gagarin became the first man in space, test pilot Harold Graham became the first human rocket. The flight was 13 seconds long.

The Bell Rocketbelt was the one that featured in the James Bond film, *Thunderball*. However, Sean Connery wasn't at the controls, because even James Bond would have trouble trying to fly this machine. Test pilot Bill Suitor stood in for 007. Suitor became so experienced at flying the Bell Rocketbelt, he also flew it into the arena during the opening ceremony of the 1984 LA Olympics – it was the most watched jetpack flight ever.

Bill Suitor flying with the Bell Rocketbelt at the 1984 LA Olympics.

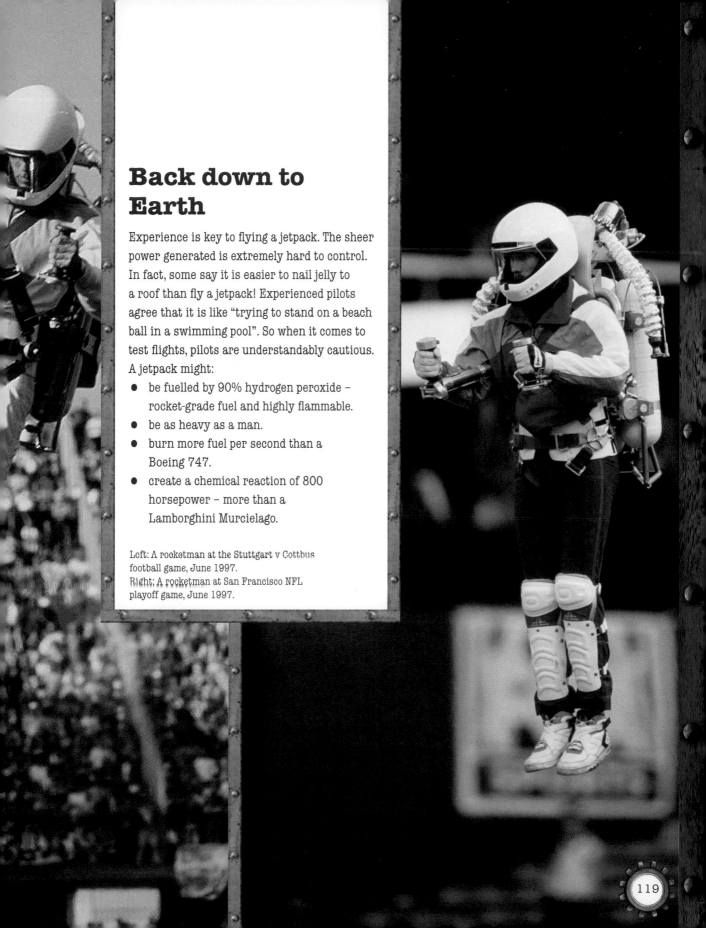

Back down to Earth

Experience is key to flying a jetpack. The sheer power generated is extremely hard to control. In fact, some say it is easier to nail jelly to a roof than fly a jetpack! Experienced pilots agree that it is like "trying to stand on a beach ball in a swimming pool". So when it comes to test flights, pilots are understandably cautious. A jetpack might:

- be fuelled by 90% hydrogen peroxide – rocket-grade fuel and highly flammable.
- be as heavy as a man.
- burn more fuel per second than a Boeing 747.
- create a chemical reaction of 800 horsepower – more than a Lamborghini Murcielago.

Left: A rocketman at the Stuttgart v Cottbus football game, June 1997.
Right: A rocketman at San Francisco NFL playoff game, June 1997.

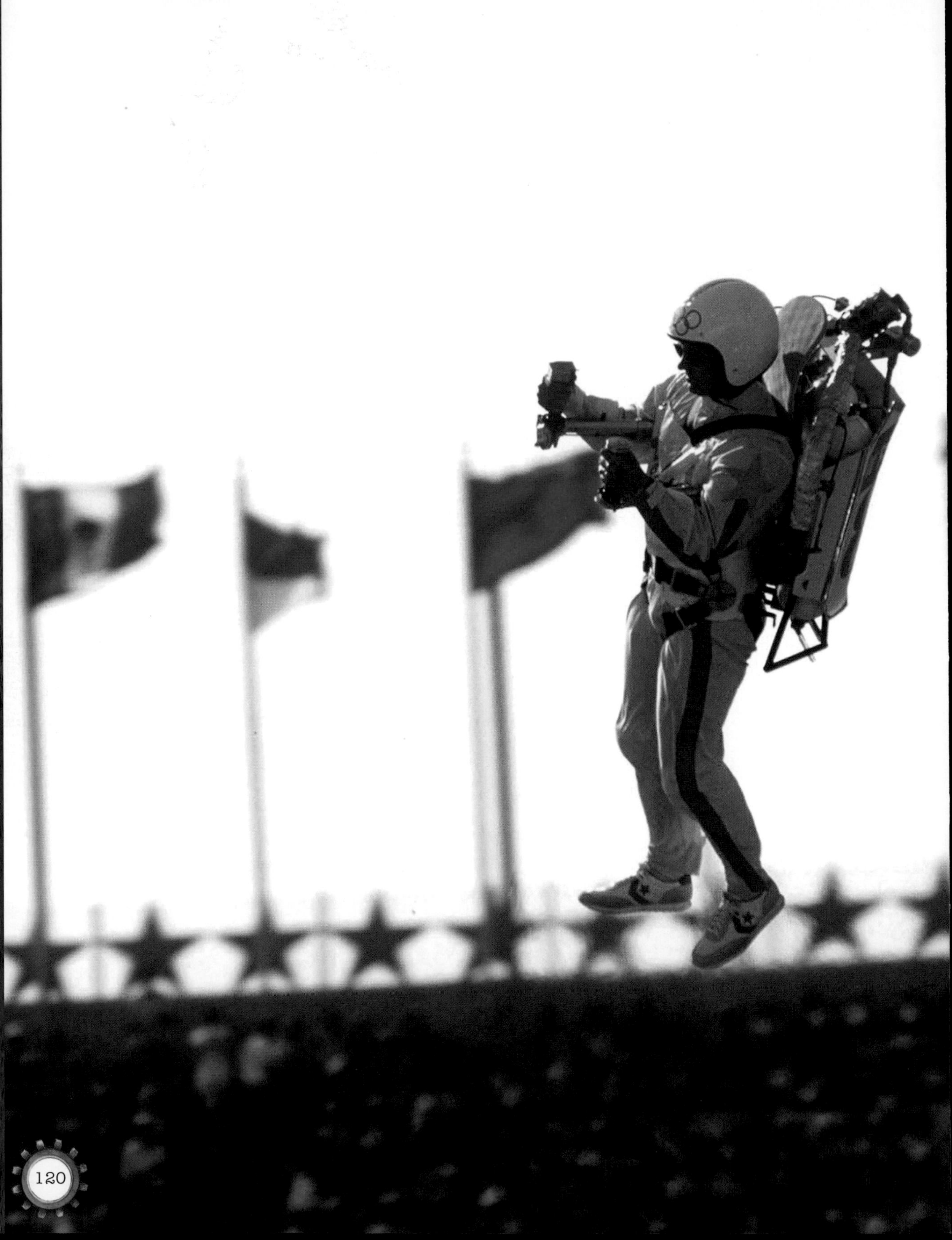

The GoFast Jetpack

The GoFast Jetpack is the most tried-and-tested of them all. Built in the US, it holds the world record for the highest speed and the longest flight – clocking 68mph and flying 1500 feet across the Royal Gorge in Colorado. The brave man who flew across the gorge is Eric Scott, the world's most experienced jetpack test pilot.

This jetpack is fuelled by hydrogen peroxide mixed with highly pressured nitrogen gas. The chemical reaction that takes place between the two creates a massive amount of heat, so steam fires out of small nozzles at about 600 degrees C and a pressure of 1200 psi. The thrust lifts the pilot and the belt into the air for the loudest, most powerful 20 seconds imaginable.

So it looks like it will be a while before we all have our own jetpack to power us quickly and effeciently to school, college, work or on holidays. What a shame, but we can carry on dreaming!

Just the thing for a hasty exit, eh Gromit?

AUTO LOCK

Opposite: Bill Suitor at the 1984 Olympics opening ceremony. Above: Rocketman Dan Schlund during a jetpack demo at Melbourne Showgrounds, 2005.

Of course, jet power isn't the only way to take off. Let's have a look at another way of getting airborne that never got off the drawing board...

Never Got off the Drawing Board...

THE MAGNUS AIRSHIP

If you've ever wondered how David Beckham makes a football curve in the air from a free kick, the chances are you haven't heard of the Magnus Effect.

This strange phenomenon occurs when objects spin through air or liquid at speed, giving them lift.

Isaac Newton was the first to describe what became known as the Magnus Effect in 1672 after watching the ball curve during a game of tennis. Almost 200 years later, German physicist Henrich Magnus described the effect after observing the flight of a cricket ball when hit with a bat. He gave his name to the effect. Since then, inventors have been trying to get the Magnus Effect off the drawing board and into their creations.

It is this curve or lift that excited inventors. If it could curve balls, then perhaps it had the potential to drive big things too.

In the 1920s, a German engineer called Anton Flettner came up with a ship design that replaced sails with giant spinning cylinders, powered by an engine below deck. He hoped that the spinning rotors would create the Magnus Effect and push the ship through the sea. And it worked! His rotor ship, the Buckau, crossed the Atlantic Ocean in 1926 and it caused quite a stir. The only problem was that the ship would have moved faster if the engine had been turning a propeller instead.

Next Flettner came up with a truly daring and revolutionary invention – an aircraft without wings. It used spinning spheres and the Magnus Effect to generate the lift to get the aircraft into the air and to keep it there. Flettner and others built a few prototypes and one actually got off the ground... only to crash soon after.

The Magnus Spherical Airship.

It was 50 years before another inventor took up the challenge. His name is Fred Ferguson and he has been working on the Magnus Effect ever since the 1970s. Instead of a plane, Fred's brainwave was to incorporate the Magnus Effect into an airship design. In the 1980s, he came up with and patented a weird and wonderful craft, which he called the Magnus Spherical Airship (see pictures below). It was a lighter-than-air craft with a large spherical envelope, filled with helium. It rotated backwards as it moved forward, creating Magnus lift. The prototype worked well and proved that as wind speed increases, rotation increases, lift increases, drag is minimized and stability increases. Ferguson also calculated that the full sized airship could have lifted 60 tonnes.

Working on the Airship.

It took 10 years to develop and cost $20 million, with funding coming from the Canadian 'Star Wars', a project to build an anti-ballistic missile defence for North America. However, when 'Star Wars' was scrapped, the funding dried up and the prototype was accidentally destroyed.

Like all good inventors, Mr Ferguson wasn't deterred. He still believed in the potential of the Magnus Effect and started to think of other ways to use it. His research and interest in alternative energy sources led him to his latest idea – a mobile wind turbine system to generate power, just like a wind farm but in the air. He has called his system MARS (Magenn Air Rotor System). The helium-filled air rotors can ascend to an altitude where the wind speeds are higher. The rotors are tethered to the ground using conducting cables that transmit the electricity generated, which can be fed into the national grid. The conversion rate is 22% extraction efficiency of wind to electricity, which competes directly with current wind turbines, but the beauty of the MARS system is that it can be put up anywhere there is wind, up to a height of 1000 feet. And the Magnus Effect? That is used to keep the rotors anchored and stable in high winds.

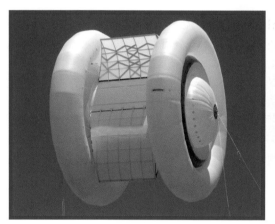

MARS.

A visual of how MARS might look over London.

Fred says "In tests we have found that the Magnus Effect will keep the airship almost vertical... the lift pushes the airship upwards instead of letting it float sideways."

At the moment Fred's air rotors are still prototypes and they currently need to be twice the size of a static turbine in order to generate the same power. If, however, they can perfect the design, Fred and his team may just succeed where other inventors have failed – to fully harness the power of the Magnus Effect and get it off the drawing board.

JEM'S MAGNUS EXPERIMENT

In order to create a Magnus Effect car, Jem used:

One DC toy motor

A plastic lemon

A toy car

A battery with voltage that matches (or is less than) the motor. For example, you should not use a 9-volt battery on a 3-volt motor or it will burn out the motor

A battery connector (if necessary)

Jem secured the plastic lemon to the axle shaft (the rotating part) of the toy motor so that it was able to spin when the motor is connected. He stuck the motor on to the front of a toy car and stuck the battery on to the back of the car. He connected the wires of the toy motor to the wires of the battery or battery connector – black to black, red to red. Then he snapped the battery connector on to the battery and the lemon started spinning. To get the Magnus Effect, all Jem needed to do was blow the side of the spinning lemon and the car moved forwards. Some of the air that is blown is picked up and dragged by the lemon as it spins, causing lower air pressure at the back of the lemon than at the front. This causes enough 'lift' to make the car move forward

Jem's verdict: "Success! A Magnus Effect car."

PS: Younger inventors should always ask an adult to help with this experiment.

CURIOSITY CORNER

GUSTAV MESMER AND HIS FLYING BICYCLES

> Inventors don't come much curiouser than this chap. He wanted to invent the 'flying bicycle'. You'd need a good cycle helmet for that!

Every two years, in the region of southern Germany known as Upper Swabia, an unusual flying festival takes place. Local residents parade through the streets of Buttenhausen riding an array of weird and wonderful 'flying bicycles' in memory of a remarkable local man named Gustav Mesmer.

This area of Germany has a reputation for inventiveness – Count Zeppelin and Einstein were both born here – but not many people outside Upper Swabia know of Gustav Mesmer or why he inspired such a strange festival.

The story begins...

Mesmer's story began in 1903, when he was born into a deeply religious Catholic family, one of 10 children. At the age of 19, he was encouraged to join a local monastery but within six years he had become so disillusioned with religion that he burst into his local church and denounced God as a fraud. His family and community were horrified and a doctor quickly diagnosed him as mad. Poor Mesmer was locked away in the infamous Bad Schussenreid hospital for the insane – a big psychiatric clinic with high walls all around it. Mesmer tried to escape many times but he was always brought back. He remained locked up for the next 35 years, seemingly forgotten by his family.

'Inventor's madness'

During these years of incarceration, Mesmer's only form of escape was his own imagination. He became fixated with the idea of flying and spent the majority of his time designing and sketching flying bicycles – thousands of them on whatever paper he could find. The staff at Bad Schussenreid scoffed at his ideas, diagnosing him with 'inventor's madness.'

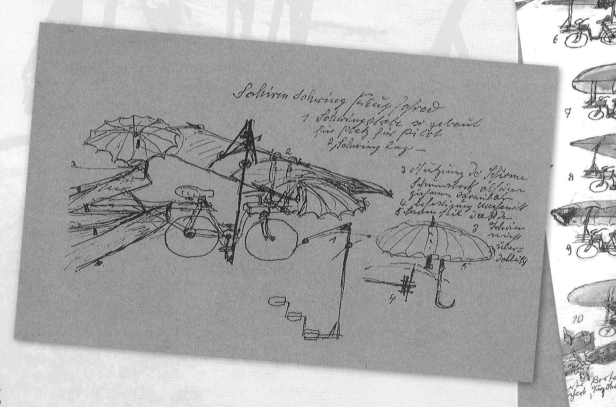

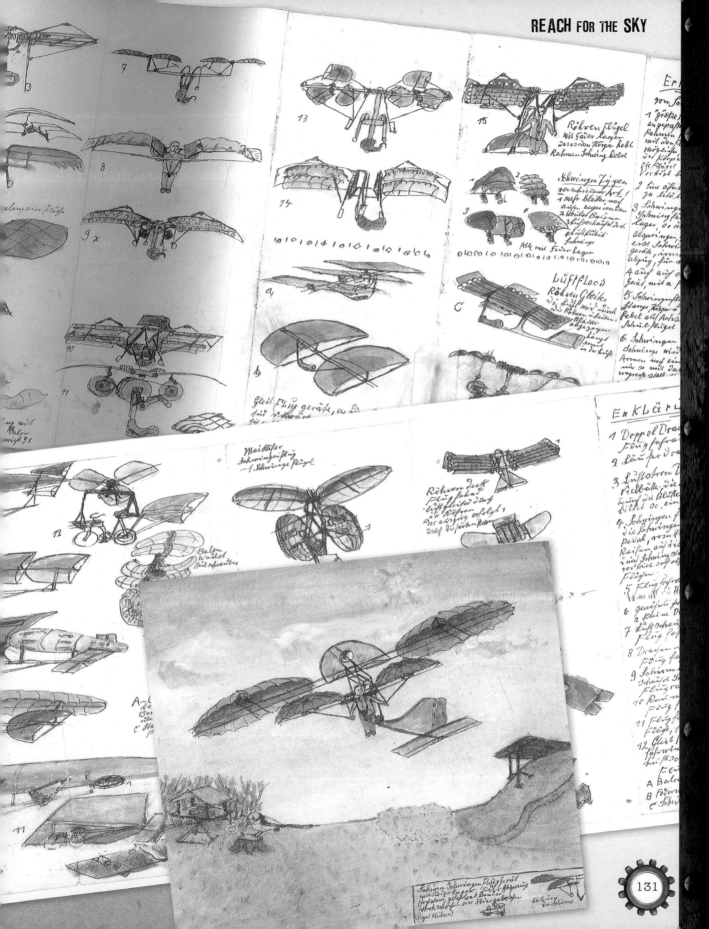

Finally, in 1964, Mesmer was allowed to go home to Buttenhausen, where he immediately began working to bring his designs to life. He adapted 10 bikes and crafted hundreds of sets of wings, mostly out of wood and plastic. He became a local curiosity, scurrying around town looking for spare parts and zipping across fields on his bicycles with wings.

Eventually his charisma and enthusiasm rubbed off on the local community. They took him to heart and that affection has survived to this day. In 1992, one of his creations was included in a display about the dream of flying at the World Exhibition in Seville. It would have been Mesmer's proudest moment.

Sarah Boger, a therapist from Buttenhausen, says, "I think he thought he was an engineer, but lots of us now think he was an artist."

The brilliance and beauty of Mesmer's inventions is not in question, but did he ever succeed in his dream of flying? Apparently yes! He said that one of his inventions once took him off the ground. Sadly, there was no one there to witness the moment.

A poem by Gustav Mesmer

When you can fly!
Mount a hill
Ascend into the air
Oh this would be so wonderful for you
Being as free as the birds
To pass the last ridge of earth in the sunshine
And flowering nature
When I hover through the air
What a wonderful feeling,
Mankind's dream is now fulfilled
Now it is only eternal life
Invent the fast wings,
They shall free you,
You shall float through the air,
Oh what happiness that would be!

Chapter 05

BETTER SAFE THAN SORRY

"Did you know that 70% of accidents happen in the home? So imagine just how dangerous a TV studio could be if you don't take proper precautions.

"Yes, accidents can happen anywhere, so in this chapter we'll be looking at inventors who have tried to make life a little bit safer for us all. There's the Hollywood superstar who came up with a wireless defence system, the underground bomb shelter created by, er, exploding a bomb and some carrier pigeons who provide an 'eye in the sky' to watch over us all.

"So mind your heads and take care not to get any nasty paper-cuts as you turn the page..."

EJECTOR SEATS

Well, let's jump straight in (or should that be straight out?) with a look at ejector seats.

Some inventions are built to operate once and once only. If your life depends on them, you have to hope and pray they work properly. That was the experience of fighter pilot Craig Penrice in 1985, when he had to eject from his plane as he was hurtling uncontrollably towards the sea at a speed in excess of 600 miles per hour.

He says, "I remember deciding to pull the handle – and the next thing I knew, I was waking up in a helicopter about an hour and a quarter later..."

Craig Penrice – two time ejector seat survivor.

Craig suffered from burns, broken bones, a dislocated finger and a severed nerve, but his ejector seat had saved his life.

Remarkably, Craig had to eject for a second time 18 years later. This time he was performing in an aerial display when his engine died. He was

over a residential area so he had to fly the plane for eight minutes until he reached a safer location before ejecting. He says it was the longest eight minutes of his life. Again, the ejector seat saved Craig's life and he is now working as a test pilot for an international aerospace company.

If Craig had been a pilot in the First World War, his experience would have been very different. Back then, the fighter planes had open cockpits and there were no ejector seats.

The first parachutes

Pioneering inventor Edward Calthorp patented his first design for a parachute in 1913 and, as war broke out, he continued to improve his design. He did offer his parachute design to the Royal Flying Corps (the predecessor of the Royal Air Force) but they turned it down. An unofficial report of the time is said to have given the opinion that having parachute devices on board the planes 'might impair the fighting spirit of the pilots'.

Other countries, including Germany, weren't quite so worried and supplied their pilots with a similar parachute to Calthorp's.

A soldier parachuting during World War II.

The catapult-able cockpit

In 1930, a Romanian inventor called Anastase Dragomir, patented a 'catapult-able cockpit'. The device had been tested successfully a year before but Dragomir did not develop his idea further. He continued to work on ejection methods and patented several versions, but died in 1966. His design became a blueprint for the next generation of ejector seats, whose development was accelerated by the Second World War. Again, it was Germany leading the way. They installed a compressed air ejection seat in their prototype jet fighter, the Heinkel He280 in 1940.

During a test flight in 1942, pilot Helmut Schenk discovered that his controls had completely iced up and he had to jettison at 7,875 feet. He was the first person ever to escape from a stricken aircraft using an ejector seat, and he lived to tell the tale. After that first ejection, approximately 60 German airmen ejected successfully before the end of the war.

In those days, abandoning a plane wasn't seen as very gentlemanly but it is probable that most pilots thought they could live with the shame rather than go down with their burning plane.

After the war, Calthorp worked to make parachutes safer and more reliable. His work led him to the idea of a device, made of compressed air, that ejected the pilot from the plane whilst still sitting in their seat. He patented his design in 1916, and although he never succeeded in getting his idea off the drawing board, Calthorp had struck on a very clever idea. Soon other inventors followed suit.

As planes got faster and faster, pilots realised that getting out of them was no longer simple. When travelling at speeds of 300 to 400 mph, the force of the air hitting an exiting pilot is over a thousand pounds – that's like being hit by a stampeding cow!

The situation is worse if the aircraft is out of control. You would probably be dead before you could pull your parachute cord, or you were in danger of being struck by your own aircraft if you did manage to bail out. Hence the need for assisted ejections became paramount.

Gunpowder-propelled ejector seat

Companies such as Saab and Martin-Baker started to specialize in ejector seat technology. Saab tested gunpowder as a propellant, rather than compressed air. The thought of being jettisoned out of a fast-moving aircraft by gunpowder might sound alarming, but for one pilot in 1946, it was a lifesaver. He had just had a mid-air collision so took his chances with the gunpowder – and survived.

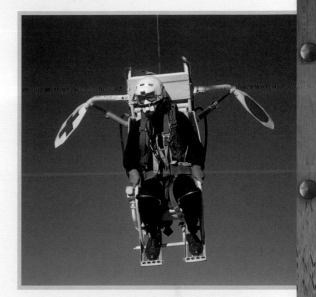

An ejector seat in use in 1955.

Martin-Baker used a solid chemical propellant, ignited inside a telescopic tube attached to the seat. Captain Bernard Lynch was the first to use their ejector seat system in 1946, in a remarkably brave test.

Ejector seats are now miracles of modern technology, driven by an on-board computer and fired by rockets. The seats fit into the cockpit by a system of rollers and rails fixed at a set angle. When the ejection handle is pulled, the seat shoots up these rails so fast that it clears the aircraft quickly and safely. The on-board computer ensures that the canopy, or roof of the plane, has been removed or a hatch in the roof has opened.

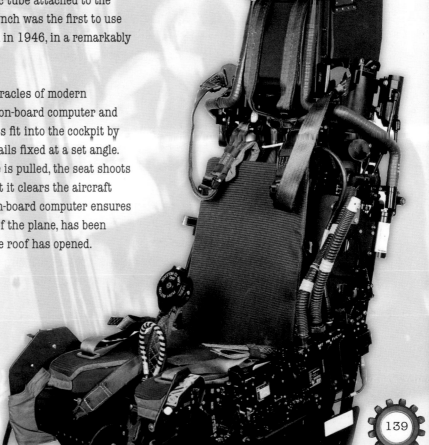

The Martin-Baker
MK16A Eurofighter
ejector seat.

139

The ejection process

Here is an example of the ejection process. All this happens in under a second!

Firing handle pulled
  Seat initiates
    Pilot restrained
      Canopy jettisons
    Seat unlocks
      Seat rises
        Pilot's legs restrained for protection
          Seat systems initiate
            Rocket motor fires seat out of plane
              Drogue parachute deploys from the seat. (The drogue parachute is a small 'chute
                that opens to stabilize the pilot and seat before the main parachute opens.)
                  Emergency oxygen flow starts
                    Altitude and speed assessed
                      If at a certain height, the main parachute from the pilot's pack deploys
                        Restraints unlock and pilot separates from seat

The pilot can then descend back to earth in a normal parachute descent. If there are two aircrew,
the process allows a split second delay before the second crew member is ejected so they don't collide.

Ejector seat testing.

Surviving against the odds

Of course, a pilot may not have any choice over where they eject and modern seats provide a survival kit as well. This contains everything from a lifejacket to sea-sickness pills and a radio locator device, so the pilot can be tracked if he or she is unconscious.

Bearing in mind that many ejections take place at high speed and that the ejection process exerts an incredible 14 gs (14 times the normal force of gravity) on the body, it is remarkable that over 90% of ejectees survive. Some have even survived after travelling at more than 1,000mph!

"It's like nothing else imaginable – and we can't train for it as the process is so violent on the body. I've heard plenty of stories of pilots ending up losing an inch or two in height after they have ejected. But if it's a choice of shortening your trousers or going down with your plane then there's no question…" Craig Penrice.

The ejector seat is an invention that no one ever wants to use, but if you do need it, you are very, very glad it is there. And it's all thanks to those inventors, scientists, engineers, computer programmers and test pilots who have worked together to make it such an incredible, lifesaving invention.

141

FLYING ROBOT SPIES

Next up, here are some feathered friends who have played a strategic role in the spy game: messenger pigeons. Well, fancy that, pigeon-fanciers!

Love them or loathe them, we are all used to the fact that surveillance cameras are watching us 24 hours a day. In fact, there are around 5 million of them in the UK – that's more per person than in any other country in the world. It is probably difficult to remember a time when we weren't under the beady eye of Big Brother, but 100 years ago, the idea of spying on someone, unseen, was the stuff of fiction.

The First World War changed that. It not only speeded up progress in transportation, weaponry and communications, it also rapidly advanced spy technology, vital to the war effort. Great military and scientific minds tried to come up with ways to find out more about the enemy. They realised how useful it would be to have a bird's eye view of the battlefields, to find out about troop movements and numbers. This sparked an idea for a crack troop of highly trained, specially equipped pigeons!

Messenger birds

During World War I pigeons were already serving alongside the troops on both sides, carrying important messages to and from the front. Pigeons can reach speeds of nearly 60 miles per hour and can fly as far as 400 miles in 10 hours, so they make excellent messengers.

Messenger pigeons were so effective that approximately 95% of the messages they carried got through to their destination. Their contribution was widely recognised and around 30 pigeons received medals for bravery. But spy pigeons? That was something else altogether.

The idea was the brainchild of a German chemist called Julius Neubronner. Neubronner was a keen photographer and he patented an invention that was a pigeon harness fitted with a lightweight camera. His aim was to send specially trained birds over enemy territory to snap up valuable intelligence. The theory was good, but Neubronner's invention was generally too heavy for the pigeons to carry and no one is sure whether one was ever sent into action – or they are just not telling!

HOW TO TRAIN A MESSENGER PIGEON

1. When a chick is four weeks old, start the training.
2. Make a new home for it in a mobile loft.
3. Spend two to three weeks moving the loft, letting the pigeon out on short flights, three times a day, so it can memorise the area.
4. At about eight weeks, send it off on longer flights to build stamina and speed.
5. After eight weeks, it is ready for action.

Flying spies

Now technology has taken Neubronner's idea to another level. Around the world, inventors are coming up with all sorts of flying spies, from bat-inspired spy planes to cyborg beetles and microflies. Most have not yet made their way off the drawing board, but surveillance drones are buzzing around our skies now. They are fast, silent and they run on rechargeable batteries instead of birdseed. One such drone is called the AirRobot. It has been built for a number of purposes, including military and police surveillance. It is satellite controlled and can be mounted with any number of devices, from video cameras, night vision or even thermal cameras. It can do almost anything that a helicopter surveillance team can do but it can access more areas, can be deployed at a fraction of the cost, and keeps personnel safely on the ground. In February 2010, one AirRobot made history by being the first unmanned drone ever to be involved in a UK arrest, using its thermal imaging camera to find a car thief hiding in a bush.

Setting up the AirRobot prior to a test flight.

WHAT THE AIrRObOT CAN DO

Vertical take offs and landings – useful when in built-up areas or on difficult terrain.

Hover and stare – it can hold a position even in strong winds.

Stabilize itself – using a combination of gyroscopic, barometric and magnetic sensors.

Move in all directions.

Land itself – if the battery is critically low.

Withstand rain, fog, sand and dust.

Specifications

Maximum flying height: 1,000m

Endurance: up to 30 minutes

Maximum weight it can carry: 200g

Maximum speed: 50km/h

Weight: under 1kg

So how would one of Neubronner's pigeon spies have compared with the flying robots? Well, it's very unlikely that pigeons were actually used in the war for surveillance. It was a great idea but the cameras were too large, bulky and heavy and so pigeons couldn't fly properly with them on. Robots on the other hand now give us the technology to spy from the air. Maybe they're not as cute as pigeons, but they're super efficient and make much less mess!

The AirRobot in flight.

WALLACE'S TOP 5 HEALTH AND SAFETY NIGHTMARES

1. It's all well and good to say that babies need plenty of fresh air, but what about this playpen that hangs out of the windows of high-rise apartment blocks? I just hope the little tyke doesn't try clambering out of his cot!

I'm all for inventions which make life a little safer, but here are some which look bloomin' dangerous, if you ask my opinion!

2. It's always the way – you get to the top of the ladder and realise you're under the wrong bulb. Well, with this Walkable Ladder you can simply totter over to the next one – just try not to wobble!

3. This chap seems to be testing the theory that a car is a safe place to be during an electrical storm. I'm not sure that I would like to be a passenger but it would be an electrifying experience!

4. Well I never – roasting a turkey with infra-red lamps! I just hope that lady doesn't lean in too close, or she'll end up with a sunburnt face!

5. This is a technique from the 1930s for teaching children to swim. Being tied to a railing seems rather scary compared to using armbands to practise your doggy paddle.

SPACESUITS

When undertaking a dangerous task, you should always wear protective clothing. And there's nothing more dangerous than going for a space-walk, so let's have a look at how astronauts take suitable precautions...

The first ever moon landing

In 1969, when Neil Armstrong stepped out of Apollo 11 and took his first steps on the moon's surface, all of humanity held its breath. It was one of the biggest moments in history. But one man at the Johnson Space Center was holding his breath for a different reason. That man's name was Homer Rheim, project manager on the Apollo spacesuit program and responsible for creating the suit Armstrong was wearing; the suit that was keeping Armstrong alive.

Armstrong was followed onto the moon's surface by Buzz Aldrin, also wearing a spacesuit designed by Rheim.

Rheim says, "I was pacing up and down the whole time. I really wasn't happy until it was all over."

Armstrong's moonwalk was the first real test of the suit. Although it had been through many simulations on Earth, the developers couldn't be 100% sure it would work. For three days, while the Apollo astronauts carried out moonwalks, Rheim was monitoring every tiny detail of how the suits were performing. Something as simple as moondust was a major problem. It was coarse and sticky and the team were worried it would damage the suits. In fact, what they learned from that Apollo 11 mission 40 years ago still influences how they build spacesuits today.

Space – the (hostile and challenging) final frontier

We are now used to images of astronauts floating in space, fixing the Hubble Telescope or the International Space Station. We are no longer amazed or intrigued by how those astronauts are able to survive in such an inhospitable environment. But that is what space is – probably the most hostile and challenging environment imaginable for delicate creatures like human beings.

Left: Buzz Aldrin walking on the surface of the moon.
Below: The Hubble Telescope.

151

The spacesuits for the historic Apollo 11 mission were made by ILC Dover, a company based in Delaware, USA. The company started its life making ladies underwear – bras and girdles – but they've been designing and manufacturing spacesuits since the 1960s.

Bill Ayrey has worked for the company for 30 years. He demonstrated what happens to your blood and bodily fluids in space in an experiment using a vacuum chamber and a balloon filled with coloured water.

The pressure drops when air is taken out of the chamber, which means the atoms in the liquid spread out so the liquid turns to a gas. This is exactly what would happen to the fluids in an astronaut's body. Hence, spacesuits are vital to their survival. Their spacesuits recreate the Earth's atmospheric pressure within a portable, enclosed habitat.

SO WHAT EXACTLY WOULD HAPPEN TO YOU IF YOU LEFT THE INTERNATIONAL SPACE STATION WITHOUT A SUIT?

- You would be unconscious within 15 seconds because there is no oxygen.
- Your blood and body fluids would boil (like when you open a fizzy drink bottle) causing your tongue to explode. This is because there is little or no air pressure in space.
- Your body tissues, including your skin, heart and internal organs, would expand because of the boiling fluids.
- You would be exposed to extreme radiation, such as cosmic rays and solar wind.
- You would have to cope with extreme temperatures – from 250 degrees F in sunlight to -150 degrees in the shade.
- You risk being hit by small particles such as dust, rock or orbiting space junk, moving at high speeds.

A spacesuit has to...

1. Recreate the Earth's atmospheric pressure.
2. Get rid of the exhaled CO_2.
3. Maintain a comfortable temperature inside the suit.
4. Block out the extreme temperatures outside the suit.
5. Guard against radiation and speeding space particles.
6. Have a communications system to allow the astronauts to talk to each other and to the control centre.
7. Have a TV camera, to record images and convey them back to Earth.
8. Allow astronauts to carry the tools they need.
9. Enable mobility and dexterity, particularly in the hands, so that astronauts can do their jobs.

The Extravehicular Mobility Unit - EMU

The current suit worn by astronauts on the Space Shuttle is called the Extravehicular Mobility Unit or EMU. It has been used in space for over 25 years and should stay in service for another 10 years. Each suit costs a staggering $12 million. Each EMU has many component parts, put together to fit each individual astronaut.

Getting in and out of an EMU is no easy feat and, when in, you have to go through a 30-step checklist before you can boldly go where few people have gone before – for a quiet walk in space.

If you are wondering how anyone can walk on the moon in a suit so heavy, you need to remember that the moon's gravity is only around one sixth (17%) of that on Earth, so it's not a problem. On Mars, however, gravity is around 38% as strong as it is on Earth so if astronauts want to go there anytime soon, their wardrobe is going to need some freshening up! They need a suit that is lighter, more flexible and easy to use – the same three things that designers have been battling with since the early days of space exploration.

So what is the future of space suits? Well one example, the BioSuit, is being developed by Professor Dava Newman. Whizz back to page 102 if you want to find out all about this development. Another example is the I-suit.

The I-suit

"The I-suit was created with places like Mars in mind." Jinny Ferl, designer.

The I-suit has been in development for over 10 years. A soft torso section replaces the hard torso of the EMU and it contains lighter metals. This makes the I-suit over 20kg lighter than the EMU. There are other refinements too, but essentially the I-suit is a 21st century EMU.

So, if human beings want to carry on the dream of exploring the universe, it can only be with the ingenuity of inventors like Jinny Ferl and Dava Newman. Or we might have to go back to the days of sending dogs into space...

Astronauts wearing the I-suit.

EXTRAVEHICULAR MOBILITY UNIT FACTS

Weight: 127kg on Earth
Thickness: 0.48cm, 14 layers
Suit construction: 14 layers of material consisting of an inner cooling garment, a pressure garment, thermal micrometeoroid garment and an outer cover. The materials include kevlar (the material used in bullet-proof vests), gortex, mylar, nylon and spandex.

Other component parts:

- maximum absorption garment – collects the astronaut's urine
- liquid cooling ventilation garment – removes excess body heat
- EMU electrical harness – provides the connections for communications and bio-instruments
- communications carrier assembly – contains the microphones and earphones
- lower torso assembly – the trousers, knee and ankle joints and boots
- hard upper torso – the hard fibreglass vest that supports the body, helmet, life support backpack and control module
- arms
- gloves – inner and outer
- helmet – a clear plastic bubble that protects the head but also ensures the oxygen is at the right pressure
- extravehicular visor assembly – this covers the helmet and protects the astronaut from extreme temperatures and flying objects. The visor is covered by a thin layer of gold to filter out the sun's harmful rays
- in-suit drink bag – providing water during spacewalks
- primary life support subsystem (PLSS) – a type of backpack that provides oxygen, power, carbon dioxide removal, cooling water, radio equipment and a warning system that lets the astronaut know if there is something wrong with the suit
- secondary oxygen pack – the emergency oxygen supply
- display and control module – displays and controls for the PLSS.

Would you believe it? A Hollywood star who came up with a torpedo-guiding system that was way ahead of its time... it's hats off to Hedy Lamarr!

Never Got off the Drawing Board...

HEDY LAMARR AND WIRELESS TECHNOLOGY

Hedy Lamarr was a glamorous Hollywood film actress. She was one of MGM's stable of stars during 'The Golden Age of Hollywood' from the 1930s to the 1950s. She was dubbed the most beautiful woman in the world, but as Hedy Lamarr herself said, "Any girl can be glamorous. All you have to do is stand still and look stupid." And Hedy was far from stupid. Along with composer George Antheil, she came up with an invention that was so ahead of its time it had no practical use. Today, we know it as the forerunner to Bluetooth – a technology used with mobile phones and computers to connect to other devices wirelessly.

However, Hedy and George were not thinking about sharing photos or MP3 files when they came up with their idea. Their motivation was a much more serious one – to protect allied forces from the enemy during the Second World War.

It seems curious that a glamorous film actress would be interested in defence technology, but there was more to Hedy than met the eye. Born in Austria in 1914, she married Fritz Mandl – the first of six husbands – in 1933. Fritz was a fascist sympathiser and millionaire arms dealer who supposedly consorted with Hitler and Italian dictator Mussolini. Hedy must have sat through many a dull evening listening to her husband and his guests talking about weapons and war. Perhaps as a result, she became staunchly anti-Nazi. She fled to America in 1937, divorcing Fritz, and soon became a Hollywood superstar and socialite. She met

composer George Antheil at one of the many glamorous parties she attended and they became good friends.

It seems that this incident was a meeting of minds. George was something of a bad boy on the *avant-garde* music scene. He had composed a piece of music that angered an audience so much that they ripped out the seats of the theatre and threw them at the orchestra! At the heart of the piece were 16 pianolas playing in time. Hedy's mother had been a pianist, and Hedy knew how to play, and strangely it was those pianolas that were at the heart of their invention.

Frequency hopping

When the Second World War began in 1939, Hedy and George started to work on their ingenious solution to a unique problem. At the time, it was tricky for a submarine torpedo to hit a moving ship at sea. It took complex mathematics to figure out exactly when and at what angle to fire the torpedo and the hit rate was low. Hedy and George's solution was to steer torpedoes using radio control. In theory, a transmitter could send signals via radio waves to a receiver in the torpedo to control its direction. However, Hedy and George also knew that radio signals were easy to intercept so the enemy could jam or block the signal. Hedy and George came up with a solution – and it was inspired by the piano rolls in pianolas. They submitted their idea for a 'secret communication system' in 1941 and received a US Patent in 1942. They called their invention 'frequency hopping'.

How frequency hopping worked

Radio waves are a type of electromagnetic radiation. You cannot see them but they are all around you. How frequently the wave peaks denotes the wavelength and the longer the wavelength the lower the frequency and the power needed to send signals. Radio control signals sent at a specific wave frequency can be picked up by receivers set to the same frequency.

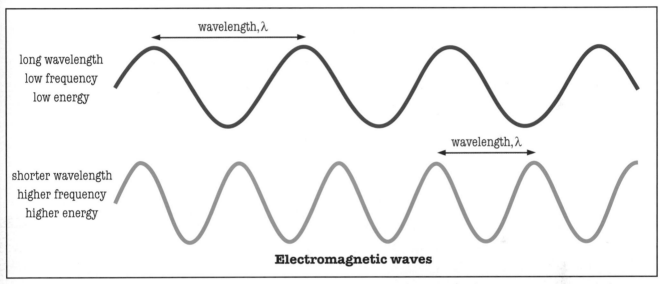

Electromagnetic waves

Hedy and George's idea was to use a pianola roll to switch between 88 different frequencies, corresponding to the keys on a piano. Pianola rolls are long rolls of paper with a series of holes punched through. Each hole represents a different note. As the roll is fed through a pianola, the keys can only make a sound when a hole allows the hammer to hit the string. Each pianola roll is 'programmed' with a different tune. In Hedy and George's secret communication system, every hole represented a different radio frequency, rather than a note. If the transmitter (on the submarine) and the receiver (in the torpedo) had identical rolls, they could communicate by switching between the 88 frequencies in perfect synchronisation, with the help of a little clockwork mechanism to turn the rolls.

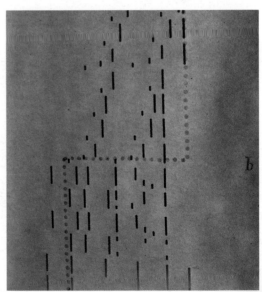

Close-up of a pianola roll.

Use of the technology

It was ingenious, but never used during the Second World War. The problem was not the frequency-hopping technology, but the fact that it was near impossible to control something by radio under water at that time. Conventional radio does not work under water because of the conducting nature of the medium. The other issue was that the war at sea was almost over by 1943, with the German fleet decimated. However, the US military rediscovered the technology, after Hedy and George's patent had expired, and used it to great effect during the Cuban missile crisis in the 1960s.

Wi-fi and Bluetooth uses

Today, this frequency hopping forms the basis of what we now called 'spread spectrum' technology. This is the technology behind Wi-fi network connections and many mobile phones. A mobile phone is in fact a short-range radio that works on a cellular network. When we make a call, the line is made secure by digital encryption and frequency hopping makes this even more robust. The technology also helps to keep the signal strength consistent – in an urban environment, there are many things that can interfere with radio waves, so this technology can switch to another frequency so the signal remains unbroken.

Bluetooth wireless technology also uses spread spectrum. When two devices have their Bluetooth turned on, they can link together using a short-range radio link to exchange information – so you can send photos or files from a mobile phone or computer to another device without the use of wires.

BLUETOOTH

Bluetooth is named after a 10th century Viking chief, who united the warring Vikings in Denmark and Norway. This unification inspired the name for the technology.

Today, spread spectrum has enabled everyone to have access to wireless technology. Previously, big broadcasters and companies carved up the radio bands between them, paying to use specified frequencies – such as BBC Radio 1 broadcasting at 97 to 99 FM. That band is exclusive to Radio 1 throughout the UK and all you need to do is tune the receiver on your radio to pick up their broadcast.

However, there are many, many bands of frequency on the radio wave spectrum and the invention of frequency-hopping spread spectrum has meant that many users can share frequencies at the same time without interfering with one another. So, we all now share radio waves, to make our phone calls, send messages and transfer information wirelessly. This is, in part, thanks to the creative, intelligent film star, Hedy Lamarr, who helped to introduce this new technology to the world.

CURIOSITY CORNER

ARTHUR PEDRICK THE ONE-MAN THINK TANK!

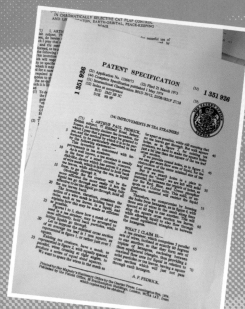

And next we're going to meet the highly prolific and rather eccentric inventor, Arthur Pedrick, whose ideas included a novel way to prevent nuclear attack...

Of all the eccentric English inventors, probably none is more curious than Arthur Paul Pedrick. He called himself a 'one man think-tank', and, along with his ginger cat, he filed over 160 patents between 1962 and 1975.

What are patents?

A patent is a licence granted by the National Patent Office to protect an invention so others cannot profit from the idea. Amazingly, the United Kingdom has had a patenting system since 1331 to safeguard the ideas of Britain's most brilliant brains. To obtain a patent, an inventor first has to prove the novelty of the idea, which was not a problem for Arthur Pedrick – his ideas were always novel.

Brian Spear, UK Patent Officer, says that "the nature of inventiveness is such that it will always attract oddballs."

Oddball ideas

A former patent examiner himself, Pedrick knew exactly what was needed to make a successful application and his ideas were unconventional and varied, ranging from 'Improvements in tea strainers' to the more ambitious 'Improvements in the irrigation of deserts by snow piped from polar regions for the purpose of minimising the impending world famine.' His patents predominantly showed a concern for the people of the world, but they also brought light relief to the patent officers.

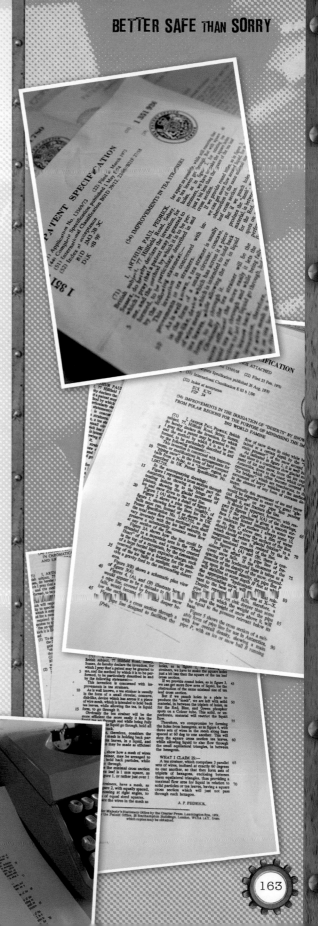

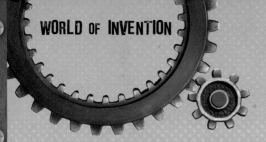

Brian Spear says, "Most of his ideas were completely off the wall. You never knew what was coming next. We would always look forward to the next one..."

One of his most ambitious and amusing patents was patent number GB 1339414. This invention is concerned with creating underground shelters for protection against an attack by hydrogen bombs (H bombs).

The underground shelters would be formed by exploding a bomb underground and the cavity produced would be fitted out with recreational and refreshment facilities (including bingo and beer). 'World citizens' would slide or parachute down the shafts onto trampolines and lifts would return them to the surface when the danger had passed.

Fortunately the cold war ended without any H bombs being dropped, but other ideas of Pedrick were spookily prophetic, anticipating events that have since become hugely important to the modern world. To overcome the energy crisis, for example, Pedrick proposed inventions such as using gas turbines to generate electricity from waste combustibles, including rubbish, paper and coke. To bring about world peace, he proposed putting a 1000 megaton bomb into Earth's orbit so if any country mounted a nuclear attack the bomb would detect the radiation and drop automatically on the aggressor. Pedrick claimed in this application that this latter idea was his cat's!

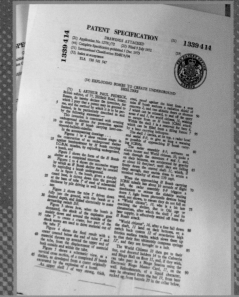

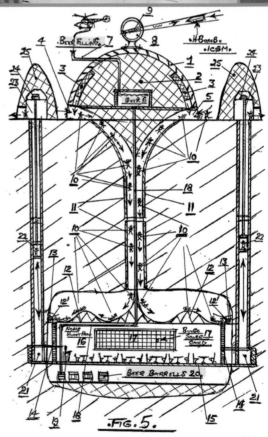

Pedrick's drawing that accompanied his patent application. It shows a helicopter topping up the beer supplies, as well as the bingo room!

Ginger

Pedrick loved his ginger cat, called Ginger (the inventor was obviously not feeling very inventive when he named his cat!). The feline frequently made appearances in Pedrick's patents, popping up in diagrams and adding the odd comment. Pedrick even wrote some of his applications in Ginger's name. According to Pedrick, Ginger had been so impressed by Pedrick's 'selective cat flap' invention – which allowed Ginger in but kept the neighbour's food-stealing black cat out – that he suggested the technology could be developed into the peace-keeping bomb.

"When I showed Ginger my drawings for the 'chromatically selective cat flap control unit' he was very impressed. 'Purr-purr,' said Ginger. 'That's quite clever. I shall be able to get in to eat my food, without worrying about Blackie from next door. But,' said Ginger, 'there is a much better use for your sensitive radiation detector device…'"

Ginger's idea was this…

"If all nuclear energy was used for peaceful purposes, instead of a large part of it being stored up for blowing each other to bits with H bombs and the like, you could all save a hell of a lot of money, which would help to stop world inflation and might even bring down the price of tinned cat food.

Pedrick and Ginger's 'selective cat flap' invention.

"The way to do it is to get some United Nations Agency to put into Earth's orbit a 1000 Megaton 'CND' Bomb, which will detect a nuclear attack below it, and be automatically programmed to fall down upon that part of the Earth's surface from which the attack originated."

When the Patent Office once invited Pedrick in to discuss the various objections an examiner had raised to one patent, Pedrick wrote back to the examiner as his cat, offering to come in to discuss the matter, provided that there were suitable refreshments on offer!

Pedrick's last patent was filed in 1975, and he died in 1977, with sadly none of his ideas coming to fruition. However, Pedrick was thought of with fondness – even affection – by the patent officers he had sparred with for so long.

"Apart from the tremendous scope and ambition of his ideas, perhaps his biggest achievement was to inject some humour into what can often be a far too deadly serious domain. Though where the line between genius, eccentricity and lunacy lies I am not qualified to judge."
Brian Spear.

PATENT SPECIFICATION (11)

(21) Application No. 17808/74 (22) Filed 23 April 1974

(44) Complete Specification published 3 March 1976

(51) INT CL² G01J 5/46 (19)

(52) Index at acceptance
G1X 14

(54) PHOTON PUSH-PULL RADIATION DETECTOR FOR USE IN CHROMATICALLY SELECTIVE CAT FLAP CONTROL AND 1,000 MEGATON, EARTH-ORBITAL, PEACE-KEEPING BOMB

(71) I, ARTHUR PAUL PEDRICK, ...tish subject, 77 Hillfield Road, Selsey, ...ssex, do hereby declare the invention, for ...ch I pray that a patent may be granted to ... and the method by which it is to be ...ormed, to be particularly described in and ...e following statement:—

...is invention is concerned with a device, ...h will respond with considerable sensi- ...to specific intensities of radiant energy ...ich it may be exposed, and thus may be ...or a number of applications in which it ...uired to, carry out an operation in ...se to specific emissions of the strength ...so called "electromagnetic wave", to ...t is directed but, in particular it can be

...o detect the difference in the colour of ...e fur on the back of a cat wishing to ...ain entrance to a house by means of a ...hromatically selective cat flap", to ...us admit to a house a cat which has ...NGER fur, but exclude a cat with ...ACK fur.

...provide, in an Earth Orbital 1,000 ...gaton Complete Nuclear Disinte- ...ion or "CND" Bomb Automatic ...risal Satellite Bomb, forming part ...n Automatic Response Nuclear ...rrent System, or ARNDS System ...ort as described in UK Patent ...,361,962, means for detecting ...certainty, whether a nuclear ...has been made on the surface ...Earth below it, and to determine ...hich part of the Earth's surface, ...ck has originated, to activate a ...through the air layer to ...the 1000 Megaton Bomb on ...ntry or state, whose govern- ...s originated the Nuclear ...he purpose of the system ...btain the release of deuterium ...m from stocks of thermo-

nuclear weapons for peaceful ...the energy therein represen... Einstein's equation $E = mc^2$.

As will be made clear, the ra... sensitive device, according to the inv... depends upon the simple process, ... occurs with respect to when light fa... moveable plates in a vacuum as occu... respect to the plates of the rotor in ... known as a Crooke's radiometer.

In the accompanying drawings:—

Figures 1A and 1B show a well know... less well known effect of radiation ... Crooke's radiometer.

Figures 2 and 3 give explanation ... above effects.

Figures 4 and 5 show two forms ... "sensitive radiation detector", accord... the invention, which, in Figure 4, depen... "photon-push" and in Figure 5 on "ph... pull".

Figures 6 and 7, show application ... radiation detector as in Figures 4 and ... chromatically selective "cat flap" operat... admit a cat of one fur colouratio... example with ginger fur, to a hous... effective to exclude a black cat fro... premises.

Figures 8, 9 and 10, show applicatio... the radiation detectors, as in Figures 4 ... to the control of a 1000 Megaton ... Orbital Nuclear Retaliation Satellite, fo... part of an Automatic Response N... Deterrent System, intended to obtai... release of the tritium and deuteriu... H bombs for peaceful use.

Figures 1(A) and (B) are suppose... represent the well known form of a Cr... radiometer, in the form of a small ... bladed motor in an evacuated bulb ... blades having black faces on one side ... silvered, or mirror faces, on the oth... usually illustrated and described in ... standard physics book.

It is usually described in the physics

Some of the patents filed by Arthur Pedrick

GB1453920	Apparatus For Extinguishing Fires in High Rise Block Buildings of Uniform Transverse Cross-Section or Plan
GB1421240	Mortarless Brick Work to Reduce House Building Costs
GB1415487	Reducing The Tendency of a Golf Ball to Slice or Hook by Electrostatic Forces
GB1391569	Miniature-Image Producing Spectacles and Binoculars
GB1388517	Electrically Operated Index and Comparison System
GB1361962	Earth Orbital Bombs as Nuclear Deterrents
GB1351926	Tea Strainers
GB1348477	Colour Television Using Light Ray Created Images
GB1340664	Variable Speed Magnetic Motor With Minimal Servicing or Maintenance Requirements
GB1339414	Exploding Bombs to Create Underground Shelters
GB1334640	Speed of Light Regulated Clock
GB1334503	Coloured Light Ray Scanning System for NTSC PAL Colour TV Transmissions
GB1333548	Internally Explosive Nail
GB1333194	Electrical Comparison Systems
GB1332079	Electromagnetically Operated Tubular Pump
GB1331862	Arrangements for Establishing a Pipe Line Across Deep Snow Subject to Frequent Fresh Snow Falls in a Manner Such That the Pipe Line Will be Retained on the Surface of the Snow Layer
GB1251780	Improvements in Tees, or Devices for Supporting Golf Balls Prior to a Driving Stroke Particularly for Practising a Golf Swing

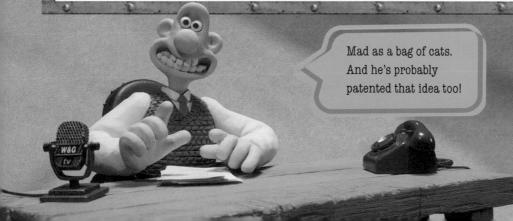

Mad as a bag of cats. And he's probably patented that idea too!

Chapter 06

COME TO YOUR SENSES

"My old gran used to say 'Wallace, you've got no sense, have you, you daft ha'porth?' Well, I don't know what she was talking about, because I have – five to be precise!

"And this chapter is all about inventions which enhance the human senses – we'll be sniffing out some bomb-detecting bees, taking a peek at some specs which let you 'see' through your tongue and going out on a limb as we look at the latest advances in prosthetics.

"So open your eyes, pin back your ears and get ready for a look-see at some sensational stuff..."

INVISIBILITY CLOAKS

Why don't we take a look at an amazing invisibility cloak? Why don't we? Because it's invisible of course...!

If you ask your friends what superpower they are most keen to possess, it's likely that high among the answers will be the power to become invisible. Just imagine, being able to snoop on all your friends, family and even famous people without them knowing that you're there.

But could there ever be a way that human beings could become invisible? Well, inventors are working on gadgets which might just help...

Professor Sir John Pendry of Imperial College London says, "I would have thought that within 5-10 years, if people really wanted to do it, then we should be able to have a form of invisibility cloak."

Professor Sir John Pendry.

The theories of invisibility

There appear to be two main theories about how objects can become invisible. The first is to use 'optical camouflage' to hide in plain sight. The second is to try to manipulate the way that light behaves so that objects do vanish before your eyes. Scientists are working on both methods in an effort to make invisibility a reality.

Camouflage

Some animals use camouflage to make themselves very hard to spot. The mimic octopus is so good at doing this that it wasn't even discovered until 1998! But the real master of making itself invisible is the chameleon. Chameleons use cells in their skin, called chromatophores to make it change colour to fit in with the surroundings. They can sense and copy the colours of the environment they're in so that they blend in and are very difficult to spot. They have evolved in this way so that they can hide from predators.

The army also uses camouflage to make their tanks, other equipment, and people blend into the environment.

Optical camouflage

At the University of Tokyo, scientists have used the natural world as their inspiration to create an invisibility cloak. The cloak is designed to blend in with its surroundings. This 'active' system of camouflage is similar to 'blue screen' technology where images are recorded and projected onto a reflective material, similar to weather bulletins on the TV. The way the Tokyo cloak works is this:

1. A camera records the environment behind the wearer. This happens in microseconds.
2. The image is sent to a computer, which projects the image onto the cloak using a special mirror, termed a combiner.

A chameleon.

The cloak is made up of thousands of very reflective beads a little like the ones found in road signs that light up in car headlights and show up at night.

It is thought that the system would not just be useful for making people 'disappear', but could also be used for larger items such as planes, cars and so on. As early as 2007, there were rumours that the Ministry of Defence had carried out tests to make tanks invisible.

Bending light

Back in the UK, Professor Sir John Pendry has developed another method of making things invisible.

The military uses camouflage to make tanks and other equipment difficult to spot.

Professor Pendry came up with a theory that it was possible to control how light behaves and to make it bend around an object. An object can only be seen if light waves bounce off it – if the light waves can be deflected then the object becomes invisible to our eyes!

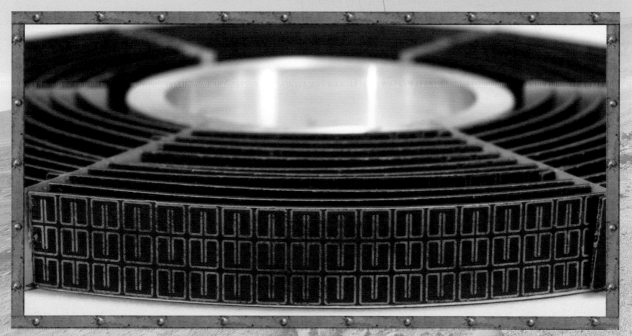

A close-up picture of the coil/cloak developed by John Pendry. This shows the intricate copper patterns that help to bend light.

Professor Pendry says, "If you can control light, then you may be able to bend it around objects – like air passing over an aircraft's wing. And if you can bend it around objects, then of course those objects themselves would physically seem to disappear, because there is no light bouncing off them and into our eyes."

A team of scientists from Duke University in the US decided to try actually making light bend and, with Professor Pendry, they came up with a working concept for a cloaking device. The concept uses what are called 'metamaterials'. These are artificial materials which 'grab' the light and make it flow around an object rather than hitting it.

Scientists are aiming to bend light around objects, a little like water going past obstacles in a stream.

A demonstration of how some things can be made to 'disappear' using the refractive index (the speed of light through a material). In this demonstration, a Pyrex test tube is filled with vegetable oil and placed into a beaker also filled with vegetable oil. The test tube seems to disappear. This is because the refractive index of vegetable oil and Pyrex is identical. Light travels at different speeds in different materials.

The cloak uses intricate copper patterns to bend light. When testing the cloak it was found that when placed over a copper cylinder the cylinder blocked nearly all the reflections and shadows from microwaves passing through it. Nearly all of the waves were guided around the cloak/cylinder and then came together again after they had gone past it, a little like water going past an obstacle in a river or stream.

So far the cloak only works with microwaves and not the wavelengths that our eyes see, but it is one more step towards the bending of other wavelengths and the possible discovery of a real invisibility cloak. Just imagine what life will be like when we can all become invisible. It could be great, or it could be quite confusing with lots of invisible people bumping into other invisible people!

TASTE GLASSES-SEEING WITH YOUR TONGUE!

And next, let's get the spec on some spectacles which respond to your taste buds...

Craig Lundberg using the Brainport system.

Craig Lundberg was a soldier serving in the British Army in Iraq. He was involved in a mission to arrest an insurgent when his unit came under heavy fire. The wall he was sheltering behind was hit by a rocket-propelled grenade and then another round struck him in the chest. Craig is lucky to be alive, but he was left blind in both eyes. Now back in Liverpool, Craig relies on his faithful guide dog Hugo to keep active and independent, but he's also getting help from an incredible new invention.

His glasses might look like an ordinary pair of sunspecs, but they are actually helping Craig to 'see' the world around him for the first time in years. The invention is called Brainport and it hotwires the brain in a way that bypasses the eyes so it is the tongue that relays visual information to the brain. This may sound like a sensory muddle, but as one of the inventors of this technology, Professor Bach-y-Rata, says, "It's your brain that actually 'sees', not your eyes." If you can accept this, the idea doesn't sound so remarkable or far-fetched.

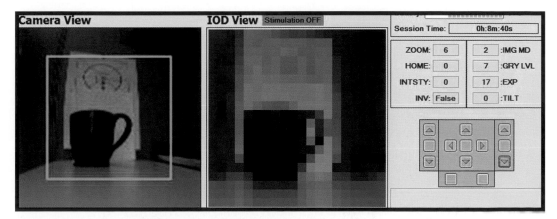

The image of the cup on the left shows how our eyes, or a camera, see the scene. The image on the right is that created by the Brainport system – still recognisably a cup but more impressionistic.

In essence, the system allows Craig to 'see' a literal version of his surroundings. It's all done through a small digital camera mounted on the glasses. The camera records what it sees and converts those images into a series of tiny electrical pulses. A small electrical base unit transmits those pulses directly to a 'lollipop' packed with 400 electrodes placed on Craig's tongue. With a bit of brain training, Craig has started to read those signals as images. He processes them in the same area of his brain that is responsible for dealing with signals he would normally receive from his eyes – known as the occipital cortex.

Craig says, "It feels like lots of champagne bubbles going off on my tongue – or popping candy."

The tongue is the perfect part of the body for the job. There are approximately 10,000 receptors on the surface of the tongue, making it extremely sensitive, and the moisture is a good electrical conductor. This combination means

that the tongue can detect a detailed stream of information coming from the glasses to the electrodes. The brain turns that information into visual images.

The invention is still a prototype and the inventors admit that those images are still rather crude. Even though there are 400 electrodes in the lollipop, it doesn't compare with the 200 million photoreceptors that a normal sighted person uses to process the visual world. However, to someone like Craig who has lost his sight completely, it could be life changing. It only took Craig a few months to learn how to use and interpret the new technology. Now he can make out familiar shapes and objects, and can navigate his way around using the visual information that his glasses emit.

Amazing as this is, Craig says, "I think it's a fantastic piece of equipment and it definitely has the potential to be life changing – but I think I'll stick with Hugo for now, I'd miss him too much if he was gone."

The 'lollipop' that is placed on the tongue.

Neuroplasticity – rewiring the brain

The 'taste glasses' are just one of the inventions that have come out of research into the concept of neuroplasticity – or to put it more simply, the idea that the brain can be rewired. To illustrate this, imagine you are driving somewhere but the bridge you want to cross is closed. You need to find a different route to get to your destination. Neuroplasticity follows the same principle – if you damage one of your senses, your brain finds another way to compensate for the loss.

There are examples of this happening with stroke victims, whose brains have developed new 'neural pathways' to bypass areas of the brain damaged by their stroke. This means that information can get to the right destination – and, with practice, the pathways get better and better. So, even if the eyes and optic nerves are not functioning at all, it is still possible for the part of the brain that interprets visual information to work from other sources. After all, if you close your eyes and someone draws a letter on the palm of your hand, you can still tell what letter it is without seeing them doing it.

We all know that the brain is a remarkable thing. Through the study of neuroplasticity, we should gradually discover more about how it works and how we can use its extraordinary capabilities.

Left: A demonstration of the full Brainport system, showing glasses, link to the lollipop, camera (on the bridge of the glasses) and the base unit.

WALLACE'S TOP 5 SENSORY INVENTIONS

1. Amazing! The ultimate portable TV - this chap can watch his favourite soap operas wherever he goes. I just hope that's a TV licence in his top pocket!

And finally, let's have a look at some incredible inventions which try to improve on our human abilities – you know it makes sense!

2. No, it's not some uncanny device to help you communicate with the Sixth Sense – these lucky people are enjoying a finger-free head massage.

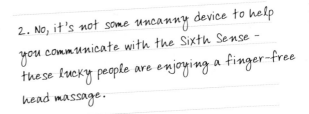

3. This clever phone picks up the vibrations from your voice-box so you can be heard in even the noisiest situation. I just hope this chap hasn't got a frog in his throat or they might think he's about to croak!

4. Look closely at this vintage jalopy and you'll see a gramophone sticking out of the driver's window. An early example of in-car entertainment - the only trouble is, it isn't actually in the car...

5. And lastly, the perfect gadget for when your eyes start to water - some windscreen wipers to stop your goggles getting wet!

181

FEATURED INVENTOR

> Next up is a man on a mission to improve the lives of people with artificial limbs...

MARK LESEK AND ARTIFICIAL LIMBS

Just before Christmas 2003, Mark Lesek was driving to his family home in Tasmania, when he had a near-fatal car crash. He remembers waking up in hospital not really knowing what had happened to him. Doctors immediately told him that they'd revived him after his heart had stopped. This news was bad enough, but then they told him that they'd had to amputate his right arm because his injuries were so severe.

Mark says, "At first I thought they were having me on because I could still feel my fingers. It was only when I looked down that I saw my arm wasn't there."

Inventing his own new arm

Mark's arm was amputated just below the shoulder and doctors told him that the amputation was so high that it wasn't possible for him to wear a prosthetic (artificial) arm. But Mark was not the type of man to accept that. Instead, he embarked on a mission to prove them wrong.

He tried out existing prosthetic arms but became frustrated with the poor range of movement they offered, and their habit of breaking down. He bought one from Germany that cost A$80,000 (approximately £45,000) but it broke down regularly and no one in Australia was qualified to fix it. He became so fed-up that he decided to invent his own new arm. He wanted to find a way to restore his shoulder function.

Mark says, "I've always been mechanically minded, and in Tasmania, we use every old bit of junk we find, so I sketched out my design on a piece of paper and got stuck in trying to build it for real."

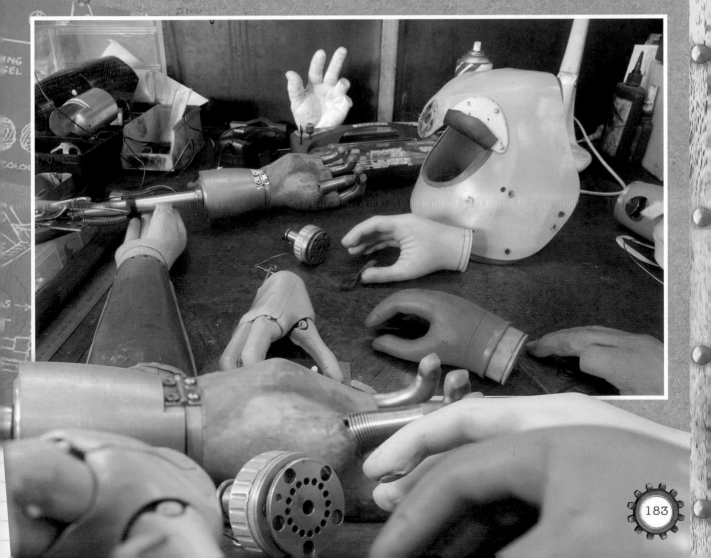

Mark was the boss of an engineering company so he used his skills and technical know-how to mix high-tech components with parts from a model airplane kit. His aim was to invent an arm that would provide him with a level of movement that would allow him to lead a normal life.

"I used to joke that I'd give my right arm for a decent prosthesis," he said.

It wasn't just movement he wanted. He also wanted to get rid of the acute pain he felt in his arm, even though it wasn't there. Many amputees feel this kind of 'phantom pain' and it can be one of the hardest things to deal with. Mark didn't experience the pain when he was wearing a prosthetic arm because his brain could see an arm there.

Osseointegration

Within weeks, Mark had a working prototype. His excitement grew while watching a TV programme soon after about a new medical procedure being pioneered in Sweden called 'Osseointegration'. He instantly knew it was the solution to his main problem – how to fix his homemade prosthetic arm to his shoulder. To attach any prosthesis to the body, an amputee would usually insert the stump of their arm or leg into the prosthetic limb. But Mark didn't have much of a stump. Osseointegration would solve that problem because surgeons would implant a titanium bolt directly into his arm bone. The bone would fuse with the bolt, allowing

him to attach his homemade arm directly on to it.

Titanium is the perfect metal for the job because the body doesn't reject it, as it does steel or aluminium. This means that the bone actually grows around the bolt to make it part of the body.

Two years, and another A\$80,000 later, Mark made the trip to Sweden against the advice of his doctors. The Swedish surgeons had taken a year to work out how to carry out the osseointegration procedure on Mark. It was the most difficult operation they had ever tried, but it was a complete success. Mark returned home to Tasmania equipped with his own titanium bolt and the difference to his life was dramatic. With his homemade arm attached to his titanium bolt, Mark has regained much of the movement he lost after his accident. His life has returned to a full and active one. But his story doesn't end there.

Close-up of the workings of Mark's artificial arm.

Mark in his workshop, using his prosthesis to control a drill.

Mark on his motorbike.

The Carnes arm

Having turned inventor, Mark is using his newfound knowledge to further develop his arm. He read about a prosthetic arm that was popular after the First World War. It was called a Carnes Arm after the inventor, William Carnes. His story was similar to Mark's. Carnes, too, lost his arm at the shoulder and decided to build his own. His design was very sophisticated and well designed, allowing full elbow, wrist and finger movements. It was way ahead of its time – better than some modern equivalents according to Mark. He is now trying to recreate a hand piece based on an original he managed to buy on the internet. He will use modern materials and technology in the hope it will work with his own arm. He hopes to produce and sell his low-cost prosthetic arms to other amputees.

Alongside this and running his company, Mark is also helping scientists at the University of Tasmania to design a robotic prosthesis, intended to be controlled by brainwaves.

Professor Tim Gales says "What Mark has achieved is genuinely incredible. He's become a real expert in the field of prosthetics, despite having no training. His expertise could potentially help amputees all over the world."

Controlling artificial limbs with the brain

With Mark's help, Professor Gales hopes to offer amputees the ability to control an artificial limb in the same way they would their natural limb – by thought alone.

They want to pre-program certain tasks, like lifting a cup or opening a door, into the arm itself. The user would then start this process by concentrating on what he or she wants to do and the arm would read their brainwaves. Mark is helping in two ways; by helping the scientists to understand the amputee's experience and by assisting with the mechanics of building the arm itself.

"I'm definitely on a mission," says Mark, "but I didn't have a choice. I just wasn't prepared to just give up on my quality of life. I hope that other people can profit from my experience and give it a go themselves."

CURIOSITY CORNER

BOMB-DETECTING BEES

Smells, lovely smells

> Now Gromit, you've probably heard of spelling bees, well these curious creatures are smelling bees! And they're performing a very worthwhile service too...

Of all the senses, our sense of smell is the most underrated. Just think how much poorer your life would be if you couldn't appreciate all the lovely aromas around you, such as fresh bread ... a roast dinner cooking in the oven ... freshly cut roses ... or the sea air. Our sense of smell plays a part in everything we do, from helping us to avoid danger to encouraging us to fall in love, yet we actually know little about how it works.

Dr James Covington, Associate Professor at Warwick University's School of Engineering, is working to build a more advanced artificial nose. According to him, smell is the sense we understand the least. We don't even have as many words to describe smells as we do to describe colours or temperature for example, and yet we have 200 times more types of smell receptors in our noses than we have light receptors in our eyes.

The complexity of the smelling system

The human olfactory (smelling) system is a highly sensitive thing. The olfactory bulb is where the brain and nerve endings in the nose meet. It is connected to areas that control memory and emotion. That is why the smell of fish and chips, for example, can instantly evoke memories of a childhood holiday. Each specific scent is made up of complex combinations of molecules and our noses can detect a scent by measuring the amounts of a certain molecule contained within a sample of air. Our brain then 'recognises' the scent.

It is the complexity of the olfactory system that makes it very hard to create technology to replicate it. Artificial noses have to be pre-programmed to recognise certain combinations of scent molecules, which means that their uses are limited. They can only detect specific scents. The first ever artificial nose was designed in Warwick University's engineering department with only one function – to tell if vats of beer had gone off. However, despite their limitations, artificial noses can have more serious and even life-saving uses than detecting stale beer.

A relatively new development is the use of devices to detect bombs. Smell receptors can pick up traces of explosives, which can trigger an alarm. They are useful but nowhere near as effective as a well-trained dog's nose. When it comes to sniffing out explosives, our canine friends are the kings of the animal world. Dogs' noses are many hundreds of times more sensitive than ours.

Right: A bomb-detecting sniffer dog at work.

Bees replace dogs

The one drawback with dog detectives is that their training is long and the cost is high. Dogs also need to rest their noses after only around 25 minutes work. So some scientists have enlisted the help of another animal – the humble bumble bee. A bee's sense of smell is every bit as good as a dog's even though bees don't actually have noses. They smell using their antennae, on which are about 170 odour receptors. Bees need a good sense of smell because they use it to find food and to communicate with each other. The antennae detect signals given off by other bees, such as an 'alarm' pheromone given off by a bee after it stings, or a pheromone given off by the queen when she is ready to mate. It is a way of transmitting information throughout the hive and it is very effective. Bees can communicate using this method from up to six miles away.

Researchers in Los Alamos, New Mexico, have now discovered a way of harnessing the bee's acute sense of smell to create swarms of 'bomb-detecting' bees.

Lovely sweet sugar

Dr Adam Hart, a biologist based at the University of Gloucestershire and the Scientific Director of the Global Bee Project, says that "the idea of bomb-detecting bees works because bees love sugar".

When a bee detects sugar, it automatically sticks out its proboscis, a long, thin feeding tube a bit like a straw, through which it sucks nectar and water. Bees can be trained to do this when they detect other odours, such as TNT or other explosives, by rewarding them with sugar every time they get it right. An infra-red beam can then be used to sense when the bee is extending their proboscis to raise an alarm in a less obvious way than using a dog.

As well as possibly being used to sniff out terrorists carrying bombs at airports, they could become crucially important in the detection of landmines in places such as Croatia, where there are an estimated 250,000 mines still buried from the war with Serbia. Tests so far have shown that it works. Placing small amounts of TNT in cups next to the bees' feeders meant that after a few days the bees would fly towards the smell of TNT thinking it was near a food source. Thermal cameras could follow the bees to pinpoint the possible location of a mine. So far the research and testing has gone well, but because mines are buried below the ground, the scent is much weaker. Therefore the bees sensitivity to the smell needs to be improved.

So what is the downside to training these bomb detective bees? They only live for a month. Nevertheless, it is still a possibility that crack teams of perfectly trained detective bees will go into active duty in the near future.

Left: Dr Adam Hart holds a bee in a drinking straw to train it to recognise a specific scent.
Inset: A bee receives its reward for recognising a trained scent – a cotton bud dipped in sugar solution.

GOODBYE AND GOOD INVENTING!

"Well, that's just about all the cracking contraptions we can squeeze in to this deluxe volume. But our book has only scratched the surface – everywhere you look you'll see the results of some boffin's ingenuity around you. And we hope you'll be inspired to come up with a few inventions of your own. You don't have to be a clever clogs to come up with a fantastic idea – it just takes imagination, creativity and a bit of hard graft.

"Why don't you take a peek at http://www.bbc.co.uk/wallaceandgromit/ and get involved building your own inventions!

"Gromit and I hope that this has given you all some food for thought. And talking about food I'm just about ready for a bite to eat – a spot of my favourite smelly cheese, Stinking Archbishop, would be just the ticket. So as Gromit rustles up a tasty snack, it's goodbye from me, from him... and fromage!

"Cheerio for now,"

Wallace